Ferrari Formula 1

Ferrari Formula 1

UNDER THE SKIN OF THE CHAMPIONSHIP-WINNING F1-2000

BY PETER WRIGHT

FOREWORD BY LUCA DI MONTEZEMOLO

ILLUSTRATED BY TONY MATTHEWS

DESIGN BY TOM MORGAN

Library of Congress Control Number: 2003106289

ISBN: 1 893618 29 3

David Bull Publishing, logo, and colophon are trademarks of David Bull Publishing, Inc.

Book and cover design: Tom Morgan, Blue Design, Portland, Maine

Printed in Hong Kong

10 9 8 7 6 5 4 3 2

David Bull Publishing
4250 East Camelback Road
Suite K150
Phoenix, AZ 85018

602-852-9500
602-852-9503 (fax)
www.bullpublishing.com

www.shell.com   www.sachs-race-engineering.de

The author and illustrator wish to thank Shell and Sachs for their support.

PAGE 2: *Enzo Ferrari always believed that the engine was the heart of a racing car. Although other parts—tyres and aerodynamics in particular—have gained in importance, that of the engine has not diminished.*

RIGHT: *Tony Matthews's working drawing of the engine cutaway is based on CAD layout drawings and numerous photographs of individual components.*

PAGE 6: *Enzo Ferrari, 1924*

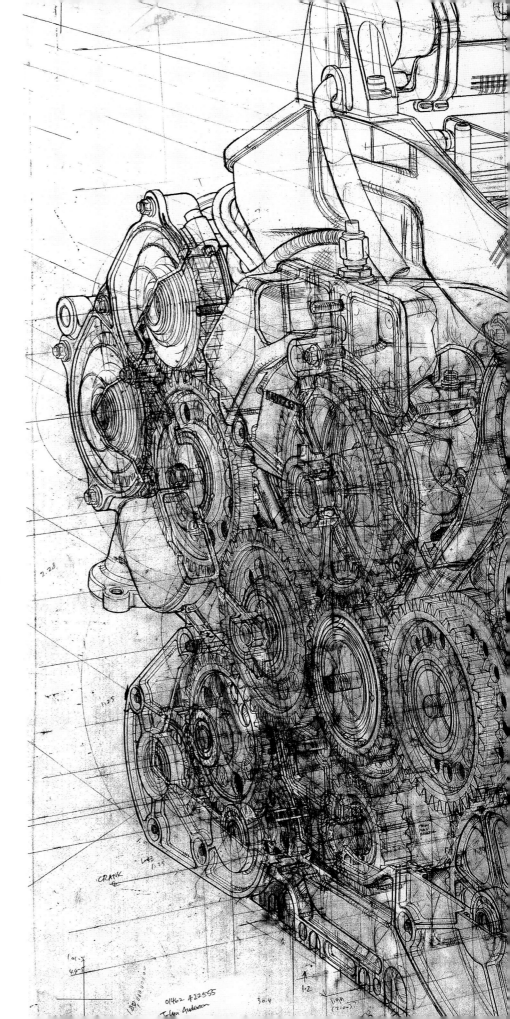

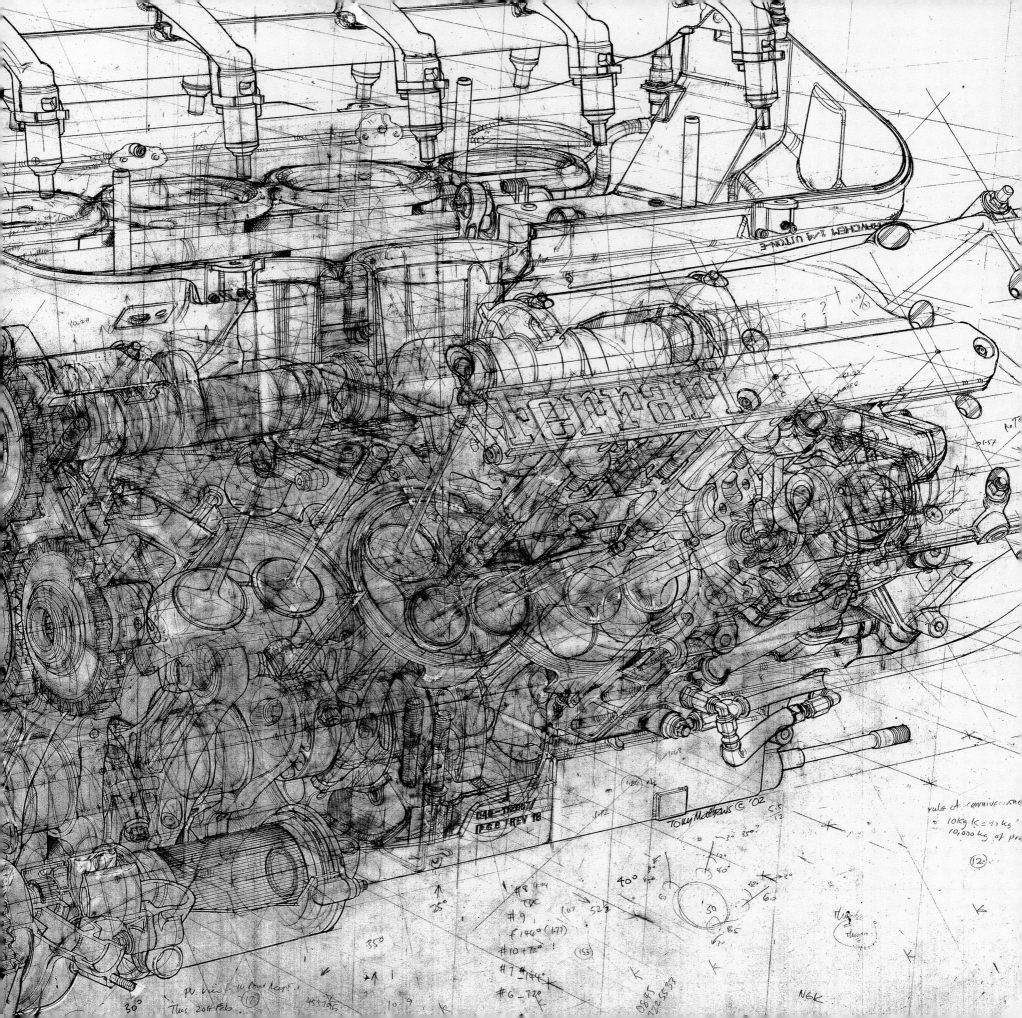

An institution is the lengthened shadow of one man.

—Ralph Waldo Emerson 1803–1882

TABLE OF CONTENTS

ACKNOWLEDGEMENTS

It is generally part of the character of people working in Formula 1 not to look back much, concentrating instead on the next race, the next car or engine, and the next championship effort. I knew from the start of this project—an attempt to describe a modern Grand Prix car in the greatest possible, or perhaps permissible, technical detail—that the real work would lie in wheedling the information out of the only people who knew it, Ferrari's senior engineers. I would be a distraction at a time when they would be focused on their current car and race programme. I also anticipated that, although Jean Todt had given the go-ahead for the book, the engineers whom Tony Matthews and I would need to talk to and ask for drawings, figures, and access for photographs would be so conditioned with preventing their secrets from escaping that they would be congenitally unable to let the information out of their hands. I was wrong.

Every one we met and dealt with at Ferrari could not have been more helpful. Not only were they interested in the project, but I quickly gained the feeling that they wanted the world to read about what they were achieving, in far greater detail than normally available in the motorsport press. Very few requests for technical details were denied, which was interesting in itself because those requests highlighted critical technologies, and quite remarkably, every promise was met. Requests were answered promptly and nothing seemed to be too much effort. No wonder they are winning championships.

Jean Todt, Ross Brawn, Paolo Martinelli, and Rory Byrne saw to it that the message went out that Tony and I were all right and could be shown everything. Without this trust, the book would simply have been impossible.

Special thanks to Regine Rettner who, with her knowledge of the right person to talk to in Ferrari, arranged meetings, managed the flow of information, and translated when necessary. She always responded to e-mails, wherever she was in the world at the time. Things happened due to her efforts, and without her keen eyes as a proofreader several errors would have slipped by us.

The list of Ferrari people who have contributed their time and knowledge can only include those we actually met. I suspect there are many more who put in time and effort to collate data and turn it into the form we wanted. Thanks to all of them, especially to Riccardo Andreoni, Giorgio Ascanelli, Claudio Berro, Angello Castelli, Luca Colajanni, Roberto Dalla, Stefano Domenicali, Marco Fainello, Leonardo Limongelli, Michael Schumacher, Gilles Simon, and Nigel Stepney.

Shell, who has been one of Ferrari's technical partners through much of its history, agreed to sponsor the book at a very early stage. Shell's generosity eased the burden of travel expenses and the costs of generating the volume of artwork incorporated in the book.

Sachs Race Engineering also agreed to provide sponsorship toward the costs of producing the book.

Technical partners are very much part of Ferrari's success, and their view on why Ferrari has succeeded has been most valuable. Special thanks to David Barnes, Kees van de Grint, Roger Lyndsay, Mike Moen, and Olaf Schwaier.

Long-time friend Bill Milliken readily offered the services of Milliken Research Associates Inc. to help with the performance analysis of the Ferrari F1-2000, without which all the descriptions of hardware would be less meaningful. Dave Segal worked long and hard to generate the performance data for the car, that forms the basis of chapter 14.

It is always a pleasure to work with Tony Matthews. His ability to take the most meagre of information and produce stunning full colour cutaways, with detail accuracy that the designers of the parts are unable to fault, will never cease to amaze me. His work has a realism to it that CAD renderings never achieve.

LAT's Peter Higham, Tim Wright, Fiona Fallon, and Matt Jennings provided beautiful and well-selected photographs to help illustrate the book's historical content. Peter also contributed circuit diagrams from his book, *The International Motor Racing Guide*. Thanks also to Toshihiko Sakon and Shigenori Ogura of F1 Modelling for supplying their handsome photos of the F1-2000.

Producing the raw material for a publication is but part of the job. Turning the text and artwork into a book that is pleasing to look at, read, and own will have just as much bearing on its success. For this I am thankful to David Bull, recommended to me as "the best editor I have worked with"—I agree; and Tom Morgan and Anna Gilbert of Blue Design, whose layout speaks for itself.

Finally, a special thank you to my wife, Hannah, who dispensed encouragement, guidance, criticism, and tolerance in just the right amounts at just the right times.

It has taken the might of Ferrari and the talents of Michael Schumacher to challenge Juan Manuel Fangio's record of five World Championships. Schumacher is the first to admit that comparing achievements nearly fifty years apart can be misleading, but it is clear that these two drivers are at a level above the others. Fangio is shown here in 1956 in his Lancia-Ferrari D50.

8

Foreword *by Luca di Montezemolo*

President, Ferrari S.p.A.

Two dates stand out to me when I think of the F1-2000. The first was February 6th, 2000. I remember that night I went down to the Racing Department to see our new race car for the first time. The next day, almost one thousand journalists, guests, VIPs, and officials came to attend the official presentation of the monoposto at Maranello. Following tradition, I would have to make a speech, pushing the objectives of the Scuderia Ferrari for the coming racing season. We were coming off winning the World Constructor's Title, the first time after a world championship drought of eighteen years. It was also the third time, in three consecutive years, that we had missed winning the Driver's Title in the last race of the season. For an automobile manufacturer like Ferrari, to win the Constructor's Title was an extremely important achievement. But we knew that we were missing the Driver's Title, which in the fans' minds, was the title. The objective we had was thus very clear: to end what was becoming a tiresome refrain of, "wait till next year." We needed to win the Driver's Title, as well.

The second date—and it cannot be any other—is the 8th of October of that same year. It was at dawn in Italy when Michael was the first driver to pass under the checkered flag at Suzuka, winning the Grand Prix of Japan and, thus, winning the World Championship one race ahead of time. The warm-up that had lasted 21 years had ended: In the golden book of champions, the name Ferrari was once again written next to the Driver's Title. The period of time between these dates was full of emotion. The first few months were exceptional—three victories by Michael in the first three races, then his success in Nurburgring and Montreal, which gave us a points lead before the series of summer races.

Then came the difficult phase, with three consecutive setbacks for Michael, lightened only by the splendid success of Rubens at Hockenheim. In Budapest, the competition overtook us in both categories; at Spa, the differences with respect to our competitors increased even more. We arrived at the Italian Grand Prix with eight points to regain in both the Driver's and Constructor's Championships. I remember very well the testing week before the race at Monza. You could feel tension everywhere in the race team; we needed to win three of the four races if we wanted to have a chance. Everyone gave it their all, and the results were obvious to see on the track. Four wins and four pole positions for Michael—plus the contribution of Rubens—gave us a fabulous double win in the Driver's and Constructor's Championships. Because of that beautiful dawn of October 8 and the weeks ahead, and then the win at Sepang, I found myself, along with the rest of the team, celebrating a magnificent season, with everyone wearing Ferrari red wigs on their heads. What joy!

This book describes all of the technical aspects of the F1-2000 by the people who made it happen and who brought us to such spectacular success. Many times, I am asked which car is the most beautiful and, if I think of Formula 1, spontaneously I say that the most beautiful car is the one that wins the most races. In the following years, we have built other exceptional race cars that have broken many records, but there is no doubt that the F1-2000 will always remain special in the history of Ferrari and will have a special place in my memories.

LEFT: *The President of Ferrari and his most valuable employee, Michael Schumacher. Montezemolo has put Ferrari back on the pedestal it occupied from the 1940s though to the 1970s, as the company that makes the best racing cars and the most desirable road cars in the world.*

RIGHT: *Luca di Montezemolo, President of Ferrari S.p.A.*

Preface

Many books and thousands of magazine pages catalogue the visible details of Formula 1 cars as they develop each year, but none peer deeply enough inside the workings of the car, engine, and transmission to properly explain how and why these vehicles have achieved ever-increasing performance. This is really not surprising. While commercial sponsorship has elevated the stakes to extraordinary heights in Formula 1 and the battle to succeed has become so technology dependent, teams and manufacturers have gone to even greater lengths

to protect their technical secrets. Indeed, some engineers are not even permitted to hold discussions about Formula 1 technology with people outside their companies, lest they reveal which topics they are interested in. In this environment it is very difficult to gather data and information to put together a book that describes in any detail the technology and engineering of a modern Grand Prix car.

Thus it was without much hope of success that I approached Ferrari's Team Principal, Jean Todt, as the Ferrari team collected the trophy for the FIA Formula 1 World Championship for Manufacturers at the end of 2000 and at the same time celebrated one of its employees, Michael Schumacher, who collected the trophy for the World

Championship for Drivers. Perhaps it was the euphoria of winning the two championships, after a fallow period of twenty-one years, but a few minutes later I had a verbal agreement from both Jean Todt and Technical Director Ross Brawn that they would cooperate on a book that described and analysed the car that had brought Ferrari back to the pinnacle of Grand Prix racing. The only condition they attached to granting me this unprecedented access was that the book not be published until four years after the car first appeared.

This is first and foremost a book about the car—the Ferrari F1-2000—as a representative of the state-of-the-art modern Grand Prix car. It is an attempt to describe the layout, functioning, and characteristics of the major components

F1-2000

of a winning car, to provide the reader with a level of detail and an understanding of Formula 1 technology that has not been achieved since Laurence Pomeroy's revelatory books *The Grand Prix Car, Vols. 1 and 2* (Ref: 0-1), were published nearly fifty years ago.

This also is a book about the team—Scuderia Ferrari—and its technical partners, upon whose specialist expertise team members also depend. Understanding how the people and companies work together and what each brings to the development of a successful car is as important as understanding the design.

Throughout the 1980s, performance in Formula 1 surged due to ground effect aerodynamics, turbo-charging, carbon-fibre-reinforced composite structures, active suspension, and computer control systems and was consequently knocked back each time with performance-restricting regulations. During this time, Ferrari lagged behind the leading British teams, unable to benefit from the technical cross-fertilisation that emanated from the close-knit but highly competitive motorsport community in the United Kingdom. It was not until Luca di Montezemolo was appointed President and CEO of the whole of Ferrari S.p.A.—the group that includes the manufacture of Ferrari road-going sports and GT cars, racing versions of these cars, the Formula 1 team, and Maserati—that the Scuderia began to climb up from its low point in 1992.

Montezemolo recruited Dr. Harvey Postlethwaite and John Barnard back to the team to lead the design and engineering department. Both British engineers had originally been hired by Enzo Ferrari in the 1980s to bring British technology to Ferrari, but they had subsequently departed to other teams. Montezemolo also appointed Jean Todt, who had led Peugeot to the pinnacles of Rallying and Group C Sports Car success, to run the Scuderia. Ferrari's performance in the World Championship started to improve, but not enough.

At the same time in Benetton, the team of Michael Schumacher, Ross Brawn, and Rory Byrne was forming and developing, leading to Schumacher's two Drivers' World Championships in 1994 and 1995. Their performance did not escape the notice of Jean Todt, who managed to recruit Michael Schumacher for 1996 and secured the services of the two engineers by the start of 1997. The improvement accelerated. Schumacher's contribution is much, much more than his ability to drive a racing car very fast all the time; his motivational forces are a major factor influencing the efforts of all who work at or with Ferrari.

Ross Brawn has described the state in which Ferrari operates as being similar to a state of war. To win a war requires the complete infrastructure of generals, officers, troops, communications, intelligence, supply, transport, administration, propaganda, and politics, as well as the latest technologies embodied in its weapons of battle. Strategy and tactics have

TOP LEFT: *A Ferrari graphic for the 2000 car.*

LEFT: *Ferrari F1-2000. The launch photograph reveals little of the new car's secrets. Ross Brawn and Michael Schumacher, however, knew its potential and exploited it by winning the first four races.*

RIGHT: *Michael Schumacher repaid Jean Todt's faith in hiring him in 1996 by winning three GPs in John Barnard's Ferrari F310.*

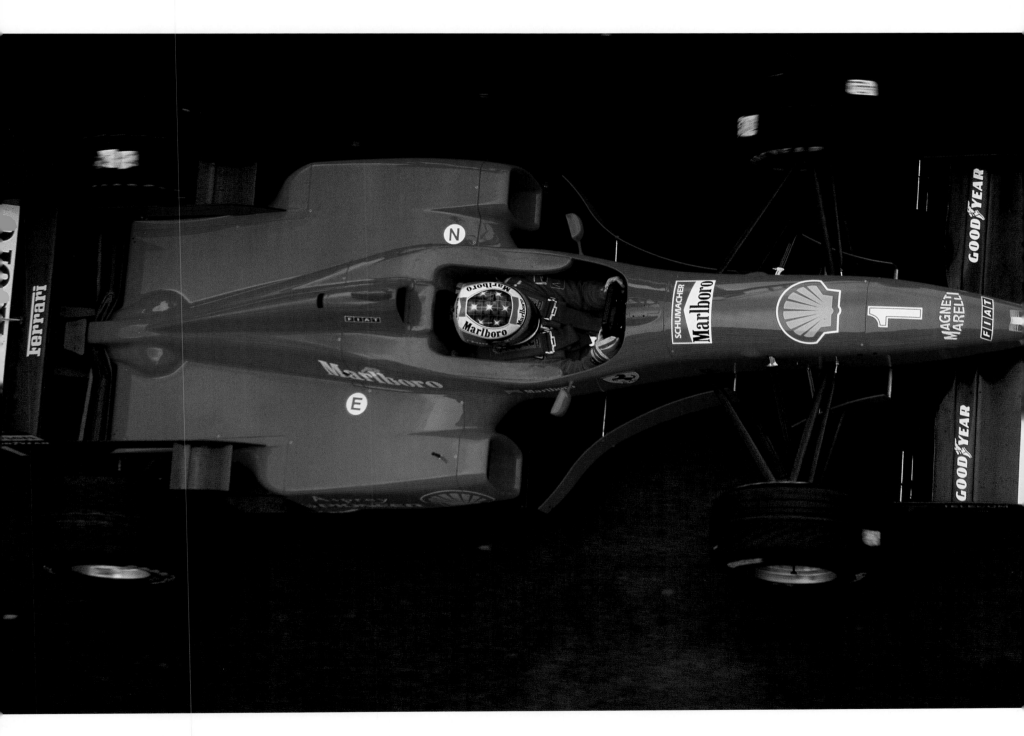

become a major part of the language of Formula 1, because the latest and best Grand Prix "weapons" can be rendered ineffective if they are not used to the optimum.

When Ross Brawn and Rory Byrne arrived in Maranello this is what they found: a well-established engine department under Paolo Martinelli, developing a competitive V-10 engine; the Barnard-designed F310, with which Schumacher had won three races in 1996; but no chassis design and engineering department. Barnard had carried out all chassis design at his base in the U.K., and the facility in Maranello had been

run down in consequence. They had to start from scratch. But they also found a large, skilled, and dedicated workforce, ready to restore Ferrari to glory, given the right direction and motivation. It took three years. Ross Brawn believes that the 2000 car was the first car Ferrari built that was not compromised by the need to use what already existed for expediency, and that truly matched Schumacher's driving skills. In the three preceding years, Ferrari had had to rely on those formidable skills in order to compete with Williams in 1997, then McLaren.

Ferrari's technical partnerships with key suppliers indicate

LEFT: *Rory Byrne, Ross Brawn, and Paolo Martinelli, the three architects of Ferrari's technical renaissance, display the mutual respect that is one key to their success at the launch of the Ferrari F1-2000 in 2000.*

RIGHT: *The Japanese GP clinched the Drivers' World Championship for Schumacher and Ferrari after a twenty-one year drought. Jean Todt collects the constructors' trophy as he adds a second Manufacturers' World Championship to his Rally and Sports Car World Championships with Peugeot.*

the prime importance of specialised technologies, the research and development of which are well beyond the resources of even the best-funded Formula 1 team: tyres—Bridgestone; fuels and lubricants—Shell; electrics and electronics—Magneti Marelli; simulation—Fiat. The industrial strength that these and Ferrari's other technical partnerships bring is enormous.

Ferrari has granted Tony Matthews and myself a rare glimpse of some of these technologies. The limits to what it was willing to reveal are set at the level that differentiates the designs of Ferrari's competitors from its own. There have to be limits, as revelation of even the smallest detail can give away Ferrari's advantage to a competitor who is working on the same problems. Those areas covered by the greatest secrecy signal what are the most sensitive and, therefore, important to the success of its cars. Even allowing it to be

known which areas are considered most secret is taking a risk. Perhaps the greatest risk has been to allow Tony Matthews sufficient access to drawings and components to draw the car, engine, and gearbox in such magnificent detail. That Ferrari has been prepared to take these risks indicates senior people in the company recognise the interest so many followers of the sport have in the technologies and engineering of the cars. Ferrari acknowledges that it has a major place in the history of Grand Prix racing and a duty to fulfil in satisfying that curiosity.

One of the difficulties in writing a book to describe a modern Grand Prix car is that many of the key technologies and technical features are no longer visible to an observer's naked eye. Photographs and detailed illustrations show design features and the layout and disposition of components, but it is not possible to deduce the characteristics of many of the parts of the car that make the greatest contributions to its performance just by examining them. Access to material and process specifications, finite element analysis (FEA) of structural components, computational fluid dynamics (CFD) and wind tunnel results, vehicle dynamics simulations, tyre characteristics derived from computer modelling and rig tests, composite layup details, fuel specifications, engine power, torque and fuel consumption curves, and electronics and software specifications are all needed to analyse how the performance is generated. It is these technologies and how they are applied to an individual car that make the difference between a design that is consistently at the front of the grid and one that is at the back. They also are the intellectual property that teams and their suppliers guard most carefully, and so access to them for study is inevitably denied till many years later.

All modern Formula 1 cars, and the Ferrari F1-2000 in particular, are highly integrated systems—each part's performance depends heavily on how it interacts with other

The stonework is very close around the streets of Monte Carlo, but the driving precision that the circuit requires, lap after lap, has made Monaco immensely popular with racers over the years.

parts. Likewise, the performance of all the individuals who make up Scuderia Ferrari depends upon the others'. Breaking down the description of the car and of the organisation that created it into discrete chapters is, in some ways, the wrong way to portray them. However, I hope readers will dip into this book even when they are too busy to sit down and read it straight through, and then pore over the drawings and photographs at their leisure. For this reason, there is inevitably some overlap between the subjects discussed in each chapter, to make it easier for the chapters to be read in any order. I trust the reader who starts at the beginning and reads to the end will not be frustrated by this feature.

I hope that this book will appeal to all Formula 1 enthusiasts who have unanswered questions about the various technicalities of the cars, to anyone involved in the design and development of any racing car, to automotive engineers in general, and to those with a passion for Ferraris.

Peter Wright
Beleymas, France

Introduction

I became interested in motor racing and Grand Prix racing, in particular, as a teenager. Initially this growing passion was fuelled by Denis Jenkinson's inspired writing in Motor Sport, but I soon sought information of a more technical nature. The school library held copies of Laurence Pomeroy's two volumes of The Grand Prix Car (Ref: 0-1), providing me with the material to study the machines that captured my increasing fascination. Unlike magazines, which are mainly populated with photographs, these books are filled with

drawings of chassis, suspension, engines, and transmissions, to be pored over and studied to reveal their inner workings. What is more, Pomeroy carried out technical analyses of the performance of the main contenders from 1895 to 1954, thus revealing why they were or were not successful. To an aspiring motor racing engineer, these books provided not just knowledge but also understanding. I have found no comparable book published since to provide enthusiasts equivalent insights into modern Grand Prix cars.

Pomeroy's books cover the period up to and including the first few years of Formula 1, the era of front-engine cars (the Auto Unions being the exception), when the main technical objectives were high power, low weight, and low drag.

The foci of the analyses were on hp/litre, hp/ton, hp/frontal area, piston area, piston speed, b.m.e.p., and maximum speed. The circuits put the emphasis on acceleration and top speed, with suspension and tyre performance being secondary. The generation of negative lift or aerodynamic downforce was not an issue.

Since the 1960s, there has been a technical revolution in Formula 1, continuing through the '70s and '80s and into the early '90s. During this period, the layout and technologies of Formula 1 cars, and in consequence many other motorsport formulae, have been established, moulded to a great extent by the FIA Formula 1 Technical Regulations. Every Formula 1 car today incorporates the following features

(the car that established the feature is in parentheses, with the date): the driver sits reclined in a monocoque chassis (Lotus T25, 1962), ahead of a single fuel tank on the centre of gravity (Lotus T79, 1978), to which is bolted a mid-mounted (Cooper, 1958) V-configuration engine as a structural member (Lotus T49-Ford Cosworth, 1967; Ferrari and BRM had explored the concept of structural engines previously, but Lotus established it as the definitive arrangement). The transmission, bolted to the rear of the engine, also carries structural loads. Wings mounted to the nose and above the gearbox (Chaparral, 1967) generate downforce that is additional to ground effect (Lotus T78, 1977), now produced by the flat undertray (FIA Technical Regulations, 1983). The monocoque is now made wholly in carbon-fibre-reinforced plastic (CFRP) composites (McLaren MP4/1 and Lotus T88, 1981). The engine is a V-10 (Honda, 1989), revving to

more than 18,000rpm, thanks to pneumatic valve springs (Renault, 1986). Electronic engine management controls all aspects of the engine, including fuel and ignition (Bosch, 1981). The transmission is operated by a computer-controlled, semi-automatic clutch and gear-change (Ferrari, 1989). Computers and electro-hydraulic control systems measure numerous parameters, optimise, and control several functions, to the extent permitted within the regulations (Lotus T92, active suspension, 1983). Belted, radial ply tyres are fitted (Michelin, 1977), almost slick treaded (Firestone, 1971), but with circumferential grooves (FIA Sporting Regulations, 1998). Carbon-carbon brake discs and pads (Brabham, 1976; originally aerospace) and clutches are universal.

The past decade has been one of optimisation and of adaptation to changing and ever more restrictive regulations, with almost nothing revolutionary or fundamental

LEFT: *The days when conceptual variation on the automobile could be tried in Formula 1 are long gone. Ronnie Peterson in Derek Gardner's P34 Tyrrell in 1975.*

RIGHT: *Mario Andretti won Lotus's last World Championship at the wheel of the Lotus T79 in 1978. The car and its ground effect aerodynamics, developed by the author, created a step change in the performance of all racing cars. In spite of attempts by the regulators to rein in ground effect, it is still a key to car performance.*

by *Chevrolet R&D, demonstrated the significance of Lift by generating downforce aerodynamically, it had been largely ignored and designers had concentrated on just the first four parameters. Tyre grip did not increase significantly until the 1960s, when tread widths started to increase, as wear rate of the narrow treads was a more critical factor until then. Formula 1 technology is about how to maximise these five parameters as much of the time as possible, and to enable the driver to use as much of them as possible, all the time. There are hundreds of technologies involved, not just in the makeup of the car and its systems, but also in the means by which the components are manufactured and in the systems for testing and racing the cars. This book is about some of the most important of these technologies.*

Making up all these hundreds of technologies are thousands of details that go into the design, the manufacturing, and the development processes involved. This book is not about these details, as they embody the main intellectual property of the companies employing them. Formula 1 has become so competitive and the stakes so high that the companies have put in place procedures that attempt to protect their secrets. Even if they allowed the cars to be photographed regularly with their body panels removed, little would be revealed as the important secrets are embedded in the fine detail of piston crown shapes, anti-friction surface coatings, damper valving, hydraulic circuits, and software. None of these are ever disclosed. The cars are retained at the end of a season in team museums or, if sold to collectors, they are stripped of their secret components. The opportunity to inspect and describe a Formula 1 car, as one could 20 years ago, has gone.

No sooner had that book been published than I found out that I had been partly wrong in my last statement. Ferrari was prepared to reveal a lot more about one of their cars than any other Formula 1 manufacturer has for more than a couple of decades, providing an opportunity to answer two questions that lie somewhere in the middle of the "hundreds of technologies" and the "thousands of details" identified above:

having been introduced by Formula 1 during this period. This is not to say that there has been no progress; indeed, the rate of development has never been greater, nor, for that matter, more costly. At least three teams—Ferrari, McLaren-Mercedes, and Williams-BMW—and maybe more are leaving no stone unturned in the quest for speed. The workings of a Formula 1 car, its engine, tyres, and aerodynamics are being analysed to reveal the remaining few secrets of how they function, and the world is being combed for appropriate technologies, materials, and processes to apply to the quest. The single technology that has brought these programmes to the current state of refinement and so greatly increased the rate at which the work that is necessary to bring the programmes to fulfilment can be carried out is the computer, along with its associated applications for measurement, analysis, design, and process control.

In my book *Formula 1 Technology* (Ref: 0-2), I write:
Only five main parameters determine the performance potential of a racing car: Power, Weight, Tyre grip (coefficient of friction), Drag and Lift (or Downforce). Until Chaparral, greatly assisted

The latest and best technologies and any amount of industrial support can lead to nothing if they are not coordinated, focused, and managed efficiently.

LEFT: *Alberto Ascari dominated the 1952 and 1953 World Championships with Ferrari, in rather the same way Michael Schumacher and Ferrari have dominated 2001 and 2002. Shown here in 1952 at the wheel of the Ferrari 500, Ascari was undefeated that season.*

BELOW: *Nigel Mansell, loved by the Tifosi, wins the Portuguese GP in 1990 at the wheel of the F1 641. Mansell benefited from Ferrari's revolutionary semi-automatic gear change system, which is now standard on all F1 cars and many road cars.*

"What is a modern Formula 1 car?" and "What does it do?" Ferrari has actually gone a little bit farther, revealing drawings and photographs of components that allow the reader to draw inferences about certain physical and visible details, even if they have not revealed all the detail specifications.

The opportunity to portray the inner workings of a modern Grand Prix car could not be passed up, even if it was not possible to do as Laurence Pomeroy had done and compare cars of different makes and across several decades. The level of paranoia in Formula 1 is such that there is no way more than one team would share many of its secrets with a single person, as had been gifted to Pomeroy. However, because the designs of Formula 1 cars have converged to an almost common layout and specification, examining just one design will hopefully portray the broader state of the art, covering all the cars on the grid, even if it is not possible to make direct comparisons of key design and performance parameters between the leading cars and engines.

If one of the smaller teams, Jordan or Minardi, had offered its car up as the basis for this book, it would have been fascinating, but it would not have been the same as Ferrari. Ferrari is special, and the F1-2000 was the definitive Grand

Prix car at the start of the new millennium. Ferrari is the backbone of Formula 1; it is the only team that has been competing continuously since the FIA created Formula 1 in 1946, and it has participated in the World Championship since it was re-created in 1950. The Scuderia has won, up to and including 2002, 159 of the 697 Grands Prix counting towards World Championship races (22.8 percent), and 12 of the 35 Manufacturers' World Championships (first introduced in 1958, under another name; 34.3 percent). Ferrari drivers have won 12 of the 53 Drivers' World Championships (22.6 percent).

The Ferrari F1-2000 is not just the car that brought Ferrari out of its long fallow period, but it is one of a series of Ferraris that are arguably the most technically sophisticated and competitive Formula 1 cars ever. Since 1979, when Ferrari last won both World Championships, only four teams have won Manufacturers' Championships—Ferrari, McLaren, Williams, and Benetton. Ferrari is the only one to have done so with both car and engine manufactured in-house.

Ferrari's progress in the World Championship during the past decade has been steady and sustained. It is more stable than the peaks and troughs of the results of its immediate competitors, McLaren and Williams. The approach taken by the current management of Ferrari, in some areas forced on them, has been to rebuild technical resources and facilities, develop close technical partnerships with key suppliers, and invest in test tracks (Fiorano and Mugello). It would appear that it is the right approach for the technical era Formula 1 is currently in; Ferrari optimises its cars using the best science and technology available.

The latest and best technologies and any amount of industrial support can lead to nothing if they are not coordinated, focused, and managed efficiently, and only people can do this. Luca di Montezemolo and Jean Todt have managed to do what many claimed was impossible: they have brought together the best of British Formula 1 expert-

ise and technology and blended it successfully with Italian industrial strength, skills, and passion. They are now moving it forward in a manner that has taken the rest of Formula 1 by surprise, raising the technical stakes. Todt realised that nothing less than the "dream team" of Michael Schumacher, Ross Brawn, and Rory Byrne, the most successful partnership in Formula 1 in the past decade, would get the job done. With the financial support of Ferrari's sponsors, Todt set out to secure their services. With Schumacher on board, he persuaded Brawn to move from Benetton and Byrne to come out of retirement in Thailand, where he was setting up a diving business. Schumacher had already shown himself to be a strong motivating force for a team, and Todt has directed that motivation in the most positive way possible within Ferrari. Understanding how the people work together and what each brings to the development of a successful car is as important as understanding the design.

It was during the research for this book, involving interviews with key Ferrari personnel and the collection of photographs, drawings, and data from Maranello since 2000, that I realised that the original aim of the book—to answer the two questions: "What is a modern Formula 1 car?" and "What does it do?"—did not go far enough. It became evident that the F1-2000 was not just the best car in 2000, but it was a single point on a curve, generated by Ferrari, of "best Formula 1 car design" that was rising consistently. Ferrari's steady improvement over the past four years has become a phenomenon not seen in modern times, and it looks set to continue. Ferrari has found the "magic formula" for success. It became evident that I needed to look more deeply at what this magic formula consisted of and how Ferrari had found it while others are still searching. The managerial and technical policies formulated and applied by Jean Todt and Ross Brawn lie at the heart of it, creating a foundation for the

sustained turn-around of the Italian team.

A broad view of the performance of Ferrari's Formula 1 cars over the past few years, up until 1998, shows that they started off at a significant disadvantage compared to their chief opposition—Williams and then McLaren. In 1999, the cars were on a par with McLaren, and in 2000, they were just superior. In 2001, they showed a marked superiority, even though the Williams-BMW-Michelin cars were faster on some circuits. In 2002, they swept all before them in a technical tour de force that sent reporters back to the history books to try and establish if and when a team had previously been as far in front. The message is that Ferrari has not only improved technically from its low point in the middle of the past decade, but it has done so at a rate markedly greater than any of its competitors and shows no signs of letting up.

Gone are the days when a designer could pull a radical new technology out of the hat, obsolescing all the existing cars overnight and leading the field until the opposition copied them, building new cars with the same technology. A few races or even one World Championship was the most reward that could be hoped for from this type of ingenuity. The era of the Lotus T78/T79 ground effect cars, the Brabham fan car, and six-wheelers is long past. The next approach, initiated by turbo engines that only road car manufacturers could afford, was about forging the right partnership with an engine supplier. It brought McLaren dominance with the TAG-Porsche engine and then with Honda. Williams replaced them by teaming with Renault in the post-turbo era, after Honda had withdrawn. More than one World Championship was possible with these partnerships, but only as many as satisfied the engine manufacturer's marketing objectives.

In the mid-1990s, the FIA established which technologies were permitted in Formula 1, a necessary measure given the explosion in performance brought about by ever-increasing

The Canadian Grand Prix in Montreal often represents a turning point in the season. In the race, Michael Schumacher finished first and Rubens Barrichello second. Schumacher gained a lucky 10 points when David Coulthard was penalised for work carried out on his McLaren just before the start.

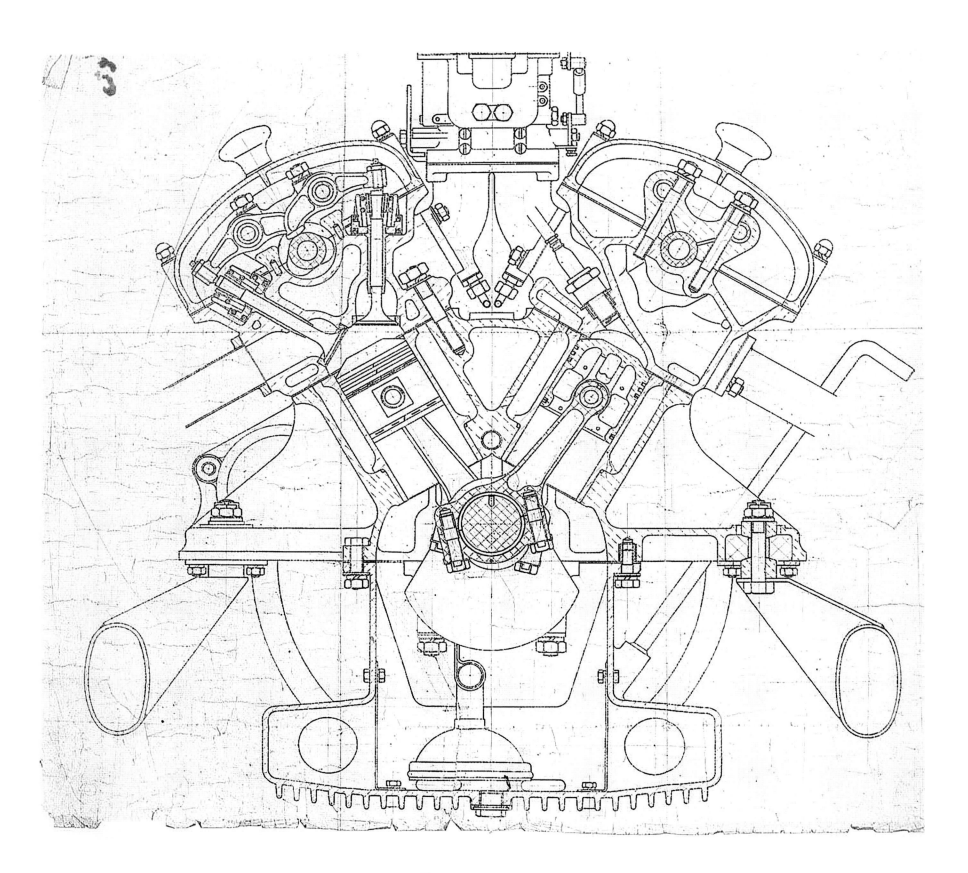

horsepower, active controls, and aerodynamic improvements made possible by huge investment in large wind tunnels. The design and engineering teams settled down to optimise and refine a well-established car configuration. The critical technologies for this work—analysis software and large fast computers—come from outside the motorsport industry and are available to anyone with the resources to obtain and run them. An adequate number of well-qualified graduate engineers are now more important than a few innovative geniuses.

With sufficient funding, the key technologies and facilities are available to any team and its engine supplier. The rate at which they are able to use those resources to improve the performance of their car is determined by what they do with them and how they use them to generate performance benefits. The greatest rate is achieved by good direction and efficient execution, and that needs the best directors, executives, and staff. Ferrari has undoubtedly found a new direction and is pursuing it effectively at a rate that has taken it from behind the opposition to a position where it is well ahead and increasing the gap. McLaren and Williams will no doubt respond, urged on by their engine partners, the

battling German luxury automobile manufacturers, Mercedes and BMW, and the others will try to do so too, from positions much farther back. The rate of improvement is not something that can be changed overnight; it may take a cultural change to initiate it, and that takes time.

It used to be conventional wisdom that a Formula 1 team that was run by someone other than its owner could never be successful. The need to justify actions would slow decisions disastrously, and the generation of internal politics would prevent success. Led by their founders, Ferrari, Lotus, Tyrrell, McLaren, and Williams took the bulk of the spoils from the '60s through to the '90s, but Ferrari without Enzo Ferrari, Lotus without Colin Chapman, and Renault (the first automobile manufacturer to take the courageous step of running its own team) failed to perform successfully with any consistency. Ferrari management has now found a way to run a Formula 1 team while also reporting to shareholders. The team is managed in a way that its technical success is not dependent on individuals and has apparently eliminated egos. It is a remarkable cultural shift that may prove very hard for the other teams to emulate. Time will tell.

1

Winning the World Championships

Dalla gestione alla vittoria (Through management to victory)

Why does Ferrari want to win the Formula 1 World Championships? The answer is simple: to sell cars. Alfa Romeo supported Enzo Ferrari's racing from the very earliest days, in order to publicise and market its road cars. When he started his own team, Scuderia Ferrari, Alfa Romeo provided the cars and the funding with the same objective. After World War II, when Ferrari made and raced cars bearing his own name, he also started to produce road-going sports and GT cars to provide funding for the racing.

LEFT: *"Winning both championships in 2000 was, for me, a dream come true," Jean Todt says. "But it was also relief; if we had not won in 2000, I do not think we would have survived."*

RIGHT: *Todt, Team Principal, carries the full responsibility for Ferrari's racing fortunes. Having seen a potential Drivers' World Championship disappear in 1999, when Schumacher broke his leg in an accident at Silverstone, Todt knows only too well that luck can play a big part in even the best-laid plans.*

To sell these cars to the rich and sporting who wished to share in the aura created by the success of Ferrari racing drivers and to justify the prices he commanded required successes on the track.

In 1969, Enzo Ferrari realised that he needed to ensure the long-term future of his company as he became older and less able to run it on a day-to-day basis, so he sold half of his company to Fiat. Fiat did not acquire Ferrari because of its potential to contribute directly to the corporation's profits; it bought Ferrari to sell Italian cars, the vast majority of which are Fiat-owned brands.

Formula 1 may create an illusion that it exists to sell cigarettes, but by far the greatest proportion of the racing teams' incomes comes from the marketing budgets of car manufacturers and automobile industry component suppliers. Even Honda, which sets great store in the technical motivation that is derived from participating in motorsport at the highest level, admitted to Ayrton Senna in 1987, "We are in Formula 1 to beat Mercedes, for they will surely enter soon."

Making and selling small numbers of sports and GT cars used to be a viable business in the 1950s and '60s, at which Ferrari, Porsche, Maserati, Lotus, Aston Martin, Jaguar, and a few other British, French, and Italian companies excelled. In the late '70s, emissions and safety legislation began to bite, pushing up the cost of certifying any car for sale in

world markets. Around the same time, the Japanese manufacturers started making sports cars, dipping into their extensive parts bins to build cars from components at volume production car costs. They sold them at lower margins than the specialist manufacturers, as they did not have to recover all the engineering and certification costs. The sports car market changed as newly well-off young people started to buy sports cars that cost little more than a saloon car, were just as reliable, and could be serviced at the local dealer of the parent car company. Specialist sports car manufacturers could not compete, and major manufacturers bought most of them to add image to their bread-and-butter brands. Only Ferrari retained a degree of independence thanks to the far-sighted

arrangements made by Enzo Ferrari when he brought Fiat into the company.

Independence does not guarantee success, either in racing or in the marketplace. The Ferrari legend was forged in the 1950s, when the fledgling constructor took on and defeated Alfa Romeo and started to build up a tally of Grand Prix victories and World Championships that has never been surpassed. The factory drivers and privateers raced the sports and GT cars, winning all the great classic races, including the Mille Miglia and Le Mans, and the queue of customers wanting to buy Ferrari road cars grew. The Ferrari name and the Prancing Horse badge became synonymous with wealth, success, and sporting accomplishment, but such an image needs polishing regularly if it is not to tarnish. The 1960s

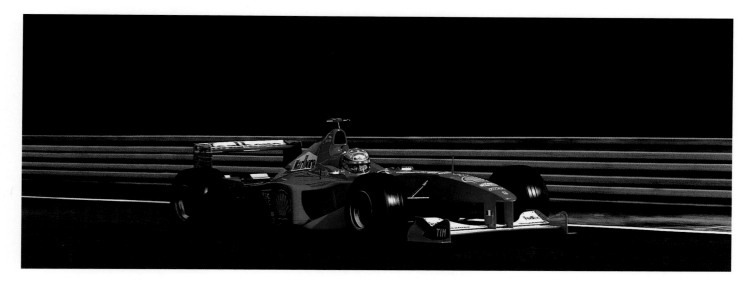

LEFT: *Enzo Ferrari started racing with Alfa Romeo, running the factory cars until he created his own Ferraris. Working with the best engineers and drivers, he learnt to obtain the maximum from both. Here he stands with one of the greatest drivers ever, Tazio Nuvolari (right), and teammate Baconin Borzacchini (left) in 1932.*

ABOVE: *European Grand Prix, Nurburgring. Michael Schumacher first, Rubens Barrichello fourth. Schumacher won a straight fight against Mika Hakkinen in the McLaren MP4/15.*

and '70s provided continued success, but as computer and aerospace technologies were introduced into Formula 1 by the British "garagistes" and Enzo Ferrari's firm hold on the direction of the company he had founded began to lessen, success on the track started to elude the red cars.

When Enzo Ferrari died in 1988, Fiat stepped in to take control of the company. The subsequent few years were the peak of the period in Formula 1 when the computers controlled the cars almost to the same extent that the drivers did, with active-everything that the designers could think up. Fiat appointed Luca di Montezemolo to take overall responsibility for Ferrari, and it was soon clear to him that if he wanted Ferrari to be a successful business selling high-priced sports and GT cars, he would not only have to revamp the range of cars and overhaul the engineering and production processes to enable the cars to compete in world markets, but he would also have to start winning again in Formula 1.

Ferrari's success as a manufacturer and a racing team did not come about because its founder was a great driver, engineer, or salesman, although during his life he had been successful at all three of these professions; it was because he was a superb manager. He sometimes described himself as an "agitator of talent"—someone who found and engaged the best engineers and racing drivers, and then "agitated" them to create excellence, either at the drawing board or at the wheel of the cars bearing his name.

Montezemolo was fully aware of the enormity of the task of bringing the Scuderia back to the top. He had been Racing Manager in 1974 and 1975, and he had won Ferrari the World Championship with Niki Lauda. With the far greater task now of running the whole company, Montezemolo needed someone to manage the racing team. He chose Frenchman Jean Todt.

Todt was a newcomer to Formula 1, but experienced in motorsport. He had been a driver and then co-driver in rallying, being part of the World Rally Championship–winning Talbot team in 1981, and representing rally drivers in Federation Internationale de Sport Automobile (FISA) from 1975. His activities had brought him to the notice of the Peugeot management, and he was asked to set up Peugeot Talbot Sport in 1982, to develop and campaign the Peugeot 205 Turbo 16 in the World Rally Championship. The cars were

"When I arrived at Maranello, I heard the whispers," Todt recalls. " 'Here's another one coming. He will come, take some money, and after one year he will go.' "

so successful that they dominated the championship in 1984 and 1985, taking the title both years. Peugeot, following a falling out with FISA, changed its allegiance to Rally Raids, winning four Paris-Dakar Rallies with cars derived from the Peugeot 205 and 405. With little else to prove in rallying, Peugeot Sport next turned to sports cars and Le Mans. The advanced Peugeot 905s won Le Mans and the World Sportscar Championship in 1992 and took a spectacular 1-2-3 at Le Mans in 1993. Its domination effectively finished off Group C sports car racing, and Todt tried hard to persuade Peugeot to move on to Formula 1. When he was unable to do so, he took up Montezemolo's offer to go to Ferrari; he already had different ideas to Peugeot's management and the desire to move on.

Born in 1946, Todt had been persuaded by his father, a doctor, to complete his studies prior to taking up a career in rallying. Now Todt understands the wisdom of that parental influence and the benefits he gained from a formal education. Once he had realised that his talents at driving were not going to take him to the top, he determined to gain as much experience in all aspects of the sport as he could, in order to fulfil his new ambition to be in charge of a team by the age of thirty-five. By becoming involved in the administration of a World Championship team, sitting on the Rally Commission of FISA, and getting to know the management of Talbot and Peugeot, he became the best man to set up Peugeot Sport, and thus achieved his target in his thirty-fifth year.

After winning everything with Peugeot, it was brave of him to decide to take on the ailing Italian team, as the first foreigner to head Scuderia Ferrari. When Todt entered the factory in 1993, Ferrari had a reputation, well honed by the Italian press, of going through one Managing Director a year. It was not expected that Todt would last more than a season, if as long as that. Todt had other ideas, believing that to manage a Formula 1 team, one needs organisational skills, experience of motorsport, contacts, commitment, and

passion, and he knew he possessed all these attributes.

"When I arrived at Maranello, I heard the whispers," Todt recalls. "'Here's another one coming. He will come, take some money, and after one year he will go.' But, slowly, slowly, after some years, they see I am still here! I wasn't giving up."

For many years, people who had had the opportunity to work at Ferrari had often speculated what would happen if the company became organised. The facilities and resources are second to none, but they were not being channeled in the right direction. The team should have won the Championship most years. Todt found a dispersed design department and under-utilised facilities. "There was a small wind tunnel at Ferrari, with dust in it," Todt says. "We were using a wind tunnel at Bristol, but every time we went there, it had to be changed from testing aircraft to testing a car. There was a feeling that aerodynamics were not so important, and we were building cars that did not have the benefit of an extensive wind tunnel programme. Now we test 140 hours per week in our new tunnel and use the little one too.

"There were rows of CAD seats, but no one using them. Now we are short of space. We do now have organisation, the right people in the right places, and everyone is pointing in the same direction."

Todt's management creed is disarmingly simple to state, but few managers have achieved it:

> *People will give their best at work if they are happy. If people respect their co-workers, both professionally and personally, they will want them to be happy too, and will help each other when there are problems.*

Clever and creative people can often fail to cooperate fully with those around them, due to an insecurity concerning their status. It is very common in Formula 1 and has

Grooved tyres were introduced in 1998 to slow the cars. The loss of tread area is graphically illustrated in this shot, taken at the European GP at the Nurburgring.

something to do with ego. When clever and creative people do cooperate with others, the stimulus they receive enhances their creative output, and whole group, working together, becomes far greater than the sum of the individuals. That Todt has undoubtedly brought Ferrari to this state, in the dog-eat-dog world of Formula 1 and in a country whose sons include Niccolò Machiavelli, is an extraordinary achievement.

In speaking with a number of people in the team, it becomes immediately apparent that they exhibit a calm approach to their work that comes from real satisfaction with their jobs. They enjoy what they are doing, they enjoy working with each other, and they state that they cannot imagine working elsewhere in Formula 1. They also show

a remarkable modesty, making no claims that, as individuals, they are the best. They believe that it is as a group they are better—that they are the best team.

Observed Todt: "All of them are good. They have knit together since 1997 and have become friends. Every year they improve, learning from each other and working together."

It is easy to gain the impression that Todt has transformed Ferrari by bringing in outsiders, non-Italians like himself, to take it over. In such an international business, with as severe a limit on the number of proven, top technical personnel as on drivers capable of regularly winning, it is inevitable that he would have to pick some from outside. However, in number they represent a small percentage of the

LEFT: *Jean Todt hoists the 1992 Le Mans trophy for the winning Peugeot 905 team. When he was unable to persuade Peugeot to enter Formula 1 and finding that his ideas diverged from the company's, he undertook the ultimate challenge and accepted Montezemolo's invitation to join Ferrari.*

RIGHT: *Detail of Tony Matthews working drawing of the F1-2000 transmission.*

workforce at Maranello; by far the majority is Italian. "Italian people are very hard working, which surprised me at first," Todt says. "I thought they were people with a good motivation and well-known craft skills, and all they lacked was management to show that they can work as hard as anyone else. Their quality of work is excellent and they will take on anything. Sometimes they are a bit disorganised and a bit emotional—it is in their blood. It is my job to organise them in such a way that these characteristics do not adversely affect what they do.

"Whatever the nature of the work, there are certain things that must be checked. Take an aeroplane that a pilot flies ten times a day from Bologna to Milano: he has to check it each flight and everything he does has a procedure. There are good reasons for this. There is a need for systems, checks, and methodology, and none of this was in place when I started."

It is a popular myth that Ferrari is a team built around and for the sole purpose of one man—Michael Schumacher. Todt, however, is quite clear about the role of his highest-paid employee: "Michael is a great guy and absolutely the number one. He is often greatly misunderstood as a person, because he can appear to be cold sometimes. He is a bit shy; he does this to protect himself and does not always show who he is to everyone. He is a fantastically hard worker; he is committed, curious about everything, asks a lot of questions, and he has passion. However, he does not command anything, as he does not have any role in the company other than driving. He does not run any part of it.

"His commitment and his credibility as a driver mean he is very much respected, and this results in him acting as a strong motivation for everyone working at Ferrari. They all want to make him happy too!"

Schumacher echoes Todt's view of his role and is adamant that he is not significantly involved in the development programmes or the design of next year's car. His job is to get the

most out of the current car being raced, and he will do whatever that takes. He puts the current success of Ferrari down to stability and attention to detail. "We have had clever and good people for a long time, but we haven't had stability for all that time," Schumacher says. "Since I joined Ferrari and since people like Ross and Rory have arrived, they have given a stable base to the technical side that has created the path for success.

"It is often small details that can cause a team to fall over

"The fun now is being the best. To go to another team after Ferrari is almost impossible, because here you have everything. If you need something, you get it; we cannot say we are without anything."

the edge or bring it back onto the road," Schumacher continues. "I have seen this in Benetton and now in Ferrari. I have seen the falling over the edge happening to other teams, like Benetton again—once it fell over the edge it couldn't get back. Maybe McLaren are there too at this time."

One person who has seen the transformation of Ferrari under Todt is Englishman Nigel Stepney. Stepney arrived at Ferrari before Todt, in January 1993, as Barnard's right-hand man at Ferrari, while Barnard concentrated on designing the cars from his U.K. base. Stepney had been in Formula 1 since the late 1970s, working for Shadow, Lotus, and Benetton,

where he met Barnard. Effectively Chief Mechanic up until 2000, he is now Race Technical Manager, coordinating the build, maintenance, and racing of the cars and liaison with the design office on all technical issues.

"When John invited me down in August 1992 to have a look around, the place was very different," Stepney recalls. "It was all very dark, and as I walked in the gate, everyone looked at me and I could see them wondering what I was doing here—most of the mechanics knew me from racing over the years. When I started the following year, we were working from two technical offices, one in Godalming, England,

and one here. The one here was doing an interim car to keep things going till the new concept for '94 came along, with its new design and manufacturing technology. It was very difficult to be in the middle of all that, and at the end of the day, it was just confusion. In the middle of '93, when Jean arrived, it started to change. He looked at people, talked to and listened to them, and then began to build up the team. He put together a group of twenty people or so, not necessarily the best people, but ones who could work together. If you put the twenty best together, you would probably not expect that to work, but twenty people at a high enough level and who will work together to improve has worked.

"In 1997 and 1998, you could start to see the results, but since then it has gone on in leaps and bounds. They are such a good group of people, ones who you can work with; nobody wants anyone else's job, and there are very few overlapping areas. It has not been over-organised, but people have been given the support, and that helps one's confidence and then you can do your job. It takes a while to find out how everyone fits in. You get to know each other's weaknesses—everyone is human—and you tend to help each other out as well as push them, which raises the level of everybody. No one wants to be left behind.

"We now have procedures for everything," Stepney continues. "We used to have a checklist that ran to one page. Now we have them for everything. We prioritise changes as they go through the system: the two top priorities are safety and reliability, and after that, things that make life easier and other modifications. I think we have become very efficient at picking out the points that are bad and resolving them quickly. You can react quickly, but react wrong. Our strength is that we react reasonably fast, but usually right.

"The quality has improved markedly in the last few years as the systems have come together. Everyone listens to suggestions; they follow up some of them and throw others out, but they do listen and consider them. I have a lot of respect for Ross in this area. We have grown fourfold since I started here. A lot of the manufacture was done outside, machining and fabrication work, and then, slowly, as material and process technologies developed, we brought it in so that we do not lose the technology. That leads to better quality control and overall control of manufacturing. The whole organisation has been overhauled and cleaned up, but has not required many personnel changes.

"The real test of the system was this year [2002] when we introduced the new car in Brazil, instead of at the start of the year. We were operating two different cars—one was brand new—and Brazil is not just down the road. If the systems had not been in place with everything working, we couldn't have done it, and certainly not won the race."

Stepney has seen many changes in Formula 1 in general, from a time when it was still "fun" to the fully professional attitude required by the global business it has become today. "The fun now is being the best. To go to another team after Ferrari is almost impossible, because here you have everything. If you need something, you get it; we cannot say we are without anything," Stepney says.

Ferrari is now back up on the pedestal, as the team to beat

BELOW: *John Surtees added a four-wheel World Championship to his seven on two-wheels, driving the Ferrari 158 in 1964. It was a closely fought battle in which he beat Graham Hill by one point.*

RIGHT: *Ferrari was the only manufacturer to be properly prepared for the new 1.5-litre Formula 1 in 1961, and it dominated the year with the Dino 156 and drivers Phil Hill and Wolfgang von Trips. Hill won the championship when Trips was killed at Monza.*

LEFT: *Niki Lauda drove for Ferrari for four years, during which Luca di Montezemolo was charged with restoring its fortunes. Lauda won World Championships in 1975 (shown here in the 312T) and 1977, and would probably have done so in 1976 but for an appalling accident at the Nurburgring.*

RIGHT: *Jody Scheckter and the 312T4 took Ferrari to the championship in 1979, the last driver to do so for twenty-one years until 2000, when Michael Schumacher finally ended the drought.*

in Formula 1. The F1-2000 was the car that finally put it there and the ever more successful cars since have reinforced its position. Ferrari has been there several times before in its history, but with so many automobile manufacturers now directly involved in Formula 1, the position has never been harder to defend. It is unlikely that Ferrari has access to better technologies than the other teams, but, at the moment, it appears to be making better use of them. Whether Ferrari is able to remain at the top depends on the strength of its management, and the crucial issue facing Todt was what would happen after 2004, when the current contracts of the key personnel, including Michael Schumacher, came to an end.

Since the intense years of 1999 and 2000, when everyone at Ferrari was totally focused on winning the championship and breaking the twenty-one-year drought, it is noticeable that the whole team is enjoying its racing immensely. Talk of retirement has faded as key personnel realise how good a lifestyle it can be to work in a happy team that is winning. Says Todt, "We are now working on the future beyond 2004. We are in a position where we are in control of the situation and we can make careful plans."

Less than twelve months after Todt made these comments to me, Ferrari has secured the services of its key personnel—Jean Todt, Michael Schumacher, Ross Brawn, Paolo Martinelli, Rory Byrne, and Gilles Simon—until the end of 2006. The fact that they have all signed up to extend their tenures at Ferrari at the same time vividly illustrates how the Scuderia is working: as a team.

It was not always possible for Todt to look ahead and plan for the future. "Winning both championships in 2000 was, for me, a dream come true," Todt says. "But it was also relief; if we had not won in 2000, I do not think we would have survived." Jean Todt did survive and is now a member of the Board of Ferrari S.p.A., with direct responsibility for all the racing activities of both Ferrari and Maserati.

Whether winning World Championships is a cost-effective way to sell cars is a very hard question for an outsider to answer. Ferrari S.p.A.'s annual report for 2000 consolidates the financial results for all parts of the group, and it makes no attempt to reveal the cost to the company of its Formula 1 activity. How much the road car division contributed to the Scuderia's budget, alongside the income from sponsors and parent company Fiat, is not possible to deduce. Although Ferrari states that 80 percent of its racing budget comes from sponsors, it is not possible to deduce whether the Scuderia "won at a profit."

thing to do, finding the people and getting them all working together. That was a good experience and a factor when we came to Ferrari and there was no chassis design group, John [Barnard] having done the car in England."

These two experiences of setting up a design and engineering team from scratch were not the only times Brawn has had to go through the process. When he joined Benetton at the end of 1991, along with Rory Byrne who was returning from the stillborn Reynard Formula 1 project, most of Benetton's design staff had left to join John Barnard, who was setting up a Formula 1 operation for Toyota—which also failed to get off the ground. During this difficult period, Brawn and Byrne forged their successful relationship, as they struggled short-handed to design a car for 1992 while building a new team. The characteristic that struck Byrne most forcibly about his new boss at that time was that he was so straightforward.

Today, advances in performance come from the sum of small increments of power, lift/drag ratio, lowering of the centre of gravity, tyre compounds, the subtleties of control algorithms, etc., painstakingly extracted from R&D and analysis programmes. Brawn has demonstrated an uncanny ability to predict, prior to a new car running extensively in testing or racing, how it will fare in the coming season. This ability is based on sound analysis of Ferrari's own new design and the measured assessment, based on careful observation of the opposition's cars during winter testing and good old intelligence from within the business, of what the opposition has been able to do since the last race of the previous season. Ferrari has raised Formula 1 technology to the nearest it has ever been to a science, and Brawn has ensured that the team has the tools to achieve this.

Brawn explains: "While we are developing the specification of a new car, we identify those areas of the current car where we can make an improvement, and the question some-

The A-1 Ring in Austria is the GP track on which the most time is spent at full throttle. Power and the car's ability to transfer it to the road are paramount.

times comes up as to whether we think we are doing enough and have made a big enough step. As always, we believe we are doing as much as we can, but is it going to be enough? The good thing is that when we feel we have made an improvement, we seem to have made an improvement, so even if we are doing nothing revolutionary, we have got a reasonable level of confidence that the next car is going to be better than this one. This is partially because some of the things are fairly predictable that they are going to be better, such as if you have more horsepower or lower the centre of gravity and you can play with the weight distribution, those are things you know are going to give you performance.

"With the aerodynamics I think we have a very good facility here and a very good group of people, so normally when they say something is better, it is better. We don't get any surprises these days from the wind tunnel. We do have occasions when a front wing may have less efficiency but better pitch sensitivity, and that is something which we would go to a few circuits and assess. We know then that we are talking about two aspects that we have got to try and quantify. Where we have a front wing that does not lose efficiency and has better pitch sensitivity, then we know we will be faster, and when we have better efficiency and the same pitch sensitivity, we will also be faster. Sometimes you have got one trading against the other, and the simulation cannot handle it, then really you have to go to the track and work through some circuits to see which way it goes. That is one area that still has to be empirically checked.

"From a structural and suspension point of view, I believe we have now got the tools to understand what we want to do there; that is something that has only come in the last few years. There was a time when you made the cars as torsionally rigid as you could, but we all knew there must be a point where it was no longer a key element, it becomes sufficiently rigid not to be an important element in the

suspension, but where was that point? You want to take weight out of the chassis and keep the same rigidity, because the rigidity is now adequate, and I feel we understand that now, and so if we want to change the torsional stiffness we know what the effect is. Those are the tools which have helped us make our decisions in the last few years, and those are the tools that we have built up here and in combination with CRF (Fiat Research Centre). They have done a very, very good job.

"This is of course on-going work, and one area where we are not really there yet is the tyre. Since towards the end of 2000, when it became clear that Michelin was going to be working with Williams and the following year with McLaren, we have realised the need to work much more closely with Bridgestone. For me, the simulation should include the tyre dynamics, the car dynamics, the whole thing, and so we measure what the car does, and we have our model of the tyre from our measurements, but unfortunately not from their rig predictions. And so we are kind of reverse engineering the tyre in the sense that, by putting enough transducers around the tyre and going out on the track, we derive the tyre properties, and then we put that back into the models to try and understand what we need. That does enable us to do a prediction of what we perhaps want from the tyre or understand what could be created with the tyre. We want to do the thing as a whole; we are not there yet but we are trying.

"While we have the ability to predict what we want structurally from the car, and how this influences the suspension, we do not have a way to develop the tyre from a structural point of view at all; to predict where the car and the tyre should be away from where it is now. We can take that tyre that we have measured and we can find ways of changing the car to try and make the tyre more effective. What we can't do is say 'What do we really want from the car and the tyre together?' We are here, optimising everything around here, should we be over there with a completely different approach. But that would need a tyre of a certain type. If we took that tyre and put it on the car, it just wouldn't work, it's bound to be worse, as we have optimised everything else around a different construction.

"We may have ten or fifteen different compounds during a season, but we have many fewer and smaller changes in construction. The car is optimised around the tyre construction, so when you change the construction, the car is no longer optimised. We have to adapt the suspension to the vertical and lateral stiffness of the tyre, but things like the load sensitivity of the tyres, front and rear, may be beyond suspension adjustments and need a weight distribution change, for instance. The trade-off between ultimate grip and tyre durability and the stability the tyres give the car are very intertwined with the car's fundamental layout and characteristics. It is a big experiment to try a different car/tyre construction, so we must have the tools to be able to think what we should do, and then be able to go round the loop and see whether we are right or wrong.

"We have started to work much more closely with Bridgestone. There are big cultural differences between the Japanese and the Europeans in the ways we work. The Japanese spend a long time deciding what to do before they do it, but once they have decided to do it, they go for it. We are a bit the other way, we tend to plough into things, and then sort ourselves out afterwards. This work is much deeper than the rest of the development of the tyre, which is very much a track thing with track people who understand racing. Now we are trying to work at a much deeper level within Bridgestone, with people who perhaps have never left Japan. It will take some time, but I think it will be very powerful when we get there—the next step for us.

"Some of our success has come from the fact that we

The Ferrari F310B of 1997 carried over much of the 1996 F310, designed by John Barnard, but benefited from Rory Byrne's heavily revised aerodynamics. The car was very quick at the Hungarian GP (shown here), but suffered from tyre blistering in the race.

have been able to create these tools and gain an understanding of the car. If we can extend that completely to the tyre, we believe we can continue to get stronger, and that is why we were so delighted when we found that McLaren was not staying with Bridgestone and we could form a much stronger relationship with them with no compromises. We believe this relationship is essential to continued success, and we are far better off staying with Bridgestone and building on this relationship, rather than swap about. We hope it will go on for a long time.

"I look at a new car and though I always want more, if the predictions say we are going to be half a second faster, then I am very happy."

Absolute performance is irrelevant in the Formula 1 World Championship. What determines who wins the title is relative performance, on average, during the seventeen races of the season. It does not matter if you are not very good, as long as you are better than the opposition, and it makes no difference if you are superb in every way if the opposition is just a little bit better. Knowing how good Ferrari really is in each area; knowing how good the opposition is, which requires good intelligence; making good any deficiencies; and deploying cars and drivers in the most effective manner at all times are among the skills of which Ross Brawn has demonstrated his mastery.

PAOLO MARTINELLI, ENGINE DIRECTOR.

Born in Modena in 1952, Paolo Martinelli is living proof that in a global business, where only the very best designers and engineers make it to the top and demonstrate their superior skills to the public by winning World Championships, it is still possible to find, educate, and develop the career of a person born locally to join that select group. Martinelli graduated in mechanical sciences at the University of Bologna and joined the road car division of Ferrari in 1978 to work in

the experimental department. Just ten years later, he was in charge of the engine department for all Ferrari GT cars.

When Martinelli was appointed by Luca di Montezemolo to take over responsibility for the Racing Engine Division in 1995, he first undertook a broad review to determine the optimum configuration for a 3.0-litre normally aspirated Formula 1 engine, including whether it should have 8, 10, or 12 cylinders. Martinelli believes that there has been little advance in the concept design of racing engines since the post–World War II engines that benefited so much from aero engine developments. The advances in speed and power and the reduction of size and weight have come about as a result of advances in material specifications (size and inertia reduction due to better properties); computer-aided analysis (size and inertia reduction due to more optimum shapes); measurements (size and inertia reduction due to better knowledge of the dynamic loads); and computer controls (optimisation of combustion, temperatures, and pressures under all conditions).

When Martinelli joined the Scuderia in 1995, it was the last year a V-12 was raced. The chassis department had lobbied its engine colleagues that a V-10 would be better from an overall car point of view, and Martinelli agreed, based on his research. The optimum cylinder size of 300 cc, almost the same as that of the 3.5-litre V-12 for which Ferrari already had a wealth of data, allied to lower friction, lower cooling requirements, and the better structural stiffness, all lead to a more optimised package. Ferrari's first V-10 was also Martinelli's first race engine, and he worked with Gilles

LEFT: *The F300 was the first Ferrari fully designed by Rory Byrne. It is shown here at Monaco, where Eddie Irvine finished third and Michael Schumacher tenth. Schumacher lost time during a lengthy pit stop to repair his suspension.*

RIGHT: *Paolo Martinelli, Ferrari's unassuming engine guru*

LEFT: Paolo Martinelli has led the development of all of Ferrari's V-10 engines to date. Rising through the engine department of the sports and GT cars, he was selected by Montezemolo to head racing engine development in 1995.

RIGHT: The V-12 cylinder block and crankcase, fabricated in titanium. One of Paolo Martinelli's first tasks on joining the Scuderia from the production car division was to research materials and the manufacturing process for engine construction. The titanium engine used the gearbox-construction technology, but proved unsuitable for allying with aluminum cylinder heads, liners, and pistons at engine temperatures.

Simon on the design of this and every engine since. The Tipo 046 had a V-angle of 75 degrees, 3 degrees wider than the ideal for a V-10, for installation reasons. He describes the year 2000's 90-degree 049 engine as a continuous evolution of the 1998 047, 80-degree V engine, and the 1999 048 that also has this V-angle. Martinelli acknowledges that ten cylinders is an odd number for an engine designer, since the twelve gives better balance and lower vibration, but it is more efficient.

The V-12 arrangement is better for the engine alone, but less good for the whole package of car and engine. Putting the requirements of the whole car before those of the engine required a major cultural shift for Ferrari, where the tradition had long been that the chassis was just a means of carrying and displaying the glorious engines. Enzo Ferrari's

contempt for the British "garagistes," with their bought-in V-8 Ford Cosworth engines, was based on this surmise and was partially the cause of the Scuderia's loss of performance through the '80s and early '90s.

It is the importance of the vibration and torsional harmonics, along with the inter-cylinder intake and exhaust interactions, that have led Ferrari to carry out the majority of its engine development on complete engines, rather than relying on single-cylinder or V-twin research engines, as used by some other manufacturers. Mercedes-Ilmor, for instance, has up to a dozen single-cylinder engines on which research and development is carried out at both Ilmor's factory and at Daimler-Chrysler.

Engine development takes place on four dynamometers,

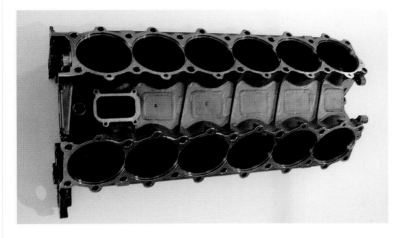

two for R&D and two dynamic ones, employing AVL electric dynamometers. One of the latter mounts the complete powertrain, including transmission, and is used for gearbox development as well as endurance running of engines. The other is set below a wind tunnel, such that the airbox intrudes into it and is subjected to aerodynamic ram pressure representative of a running car. The ability to simulate all running conditions except longitudinal and lateral acceleration, which particularly affects oil scavenging in both engine and gearbox, is a major part of Ferrari's philosophy of not track-testing components until they have been proven for performance and reliability in the rig test laboratories.

"There were three evolutions of the engine during the 2000 season," Martinelli says, "mainly changes to the crankshaft, pistons, cam profiles, intake and exhaust ducts, and, of course, mapping. Having proved a development on the dyno and in track testing, we would use it first in qualifying three or four times before racing it. This is the limit of our qualifying engines—we did not build engines that only ever get used in qualifying."

Martinelli emphasises that it is the steady development of materials, new manufacturing processes, and understanding how to apply these processes that paces much of engine development. "Every part of the engine is designed for a certain rpm—pistons, rods, crank, and valve gear—and we have to trade off rpm, power, friction, and weight. The components are so optimised that it is only more accurate predictions of the stresses and better-realised material properties in the finished component that allow us to progress. Peak

stresses occur when the internal components vibrate at their maximum amplitude, and so we are always looking at the arrangement of the engine—V-angle, firing order, cam profiles, etc.—to control the amplitude and frequency of vibration."

When Martinelli first joined the Scuderia, a die-cast stainless steel crankcase was being experimented with for the V-12 engine then being raced. The expensive tooling required for die-casting was essential to maintain close tolerances in the cast component. At that time, sand-casting tolerances and quality were such that cast components had to be designed with additional wall thickness to compensate for these uncertainties. In 1995, Martinelli built a fabricated titanium V-12 crankcase and block, based on the gearbox construction technology. He says: "It was perfectly feasible to make a crankcase in this way, and there are certain advantages in weight; however, there are also certain issues of expansion that make it unsuitable. Titanium and aluminium have different coefficients of thermal expansion, and so piston clearances and the joints with the heads become problems."

Investment casting, a technique in which a wax master pattern is sprayed with ceramic and the wax melted out to form an accurate mould, used for some years by the aerospace industry, has become a practical process for many of the engine castings since rapid prototyping systems came into widespread use. Prototype and even small batches of castings can be made in this way before committing to steel tools. Now all the aluminium castings in the engine, with the exception of the cylinder heads, are made by this process.

It is easy to overlook Paolo Martinelli's and his engine group's contribution to the turnaround of Ferrari's Formula 1 fortunes. He was already established as the head of engines when Todt arrived and brought in the already proven chassis-driver partnership of Brawn, Byrne, and Schumacher. His engines were already competitive with the opposition, and so the focus of change was on the others, who

tended to gain the most attention in the press. However, he has successfully integrated his team with the new management, and Brawn gives full credit to the engines' contribution to the team's renewed ability to win consistently.

Martinelli is a quiet and unassuming Italian who, without the benefits of a major automobile manufacturer to pour technical resources into the development of his engines (Fiat does not get significantly involved in Ferrari's engine development) and without making any claims for the power output of the products of the Racing Engine Division, has proven that he is the best when it comes to winning Grands Prix. The racing engines of the Prancing Horse are truly bred in the province of Modena, Italy.

RORY BYRNE, HEAD OF VEHICLE PLANNING.
Born in Pretoria, South Africa, in 1944, Rory Byrne set out on a career in industrial chemistry, equipped with a degree from Witwatersrand University. His working life started in 1965 with four years as chief chemist in a plastics manufacturing company near Johannesburg. Byrne's hobbies—even while still at school, he was interested in model gliders and amateur motorsports—showed early signs of his potential to become the world's most successful racing car designer years later. A small clue that Byrne would be so capable lies in the almost full marks he achieved in applied mathematics in his degree exam.

Byrne's strong competitive spirit was allied to an emerging interest in aerodynamics in his spare time. While still at school, he designed and made half-metre-span model gliders and entered them in a competition that was held around the world, the local results being sent in to a central organisation that calculated the winner. At seventeen, Byrne won his first of many World Championships as designer, manufacturer, and pilot. The following year he was second, and he won again the year after.

LEFT: *Rory Byrne with the Benetton B194 in 1994. That season announced the coming of age of the formidable combination of Michael Schumacher, Ross Brawn, and Byrne and the first of five World Championships for the trio. The Benetton won with its Cosworth-Ford V-8 against the Renault V-10 and Ferrari V-12.*

RIGHT: *Ayrton Senna so nearly won the 1984 Monaco GP, proving to the world his own talent and that of the Toleman TG184's designer, Rory Byrne.*

During the same period, Byrne developed an under-standing of motor mechanics, servicing and tuning a Ford Anglia 105E to the peak of performance, which inevitably led to racing it. He discovered that driving was not his forte: "I can put one reasonably decent lap together, but I can't keep it up for lap after lap." So he handed this role over to a friend and concentrated on the technical side. Early suc-cess in South Africa's active club scene encouraged Byrne to get more involved, progressing quickly to single-seaters and setting up a road and racing speed equipment company, Auto Drag and Speed Den. In 1971, the company campaigned a Formula Ford, designed and built by Byrne in the garage of his parents' home, which competed successfully in the South African Championship against imported British machinery. In spite of his having no formal training or pre-vious experience in mechanical or automotive engineering, the mathematics and experimental techniques he had learned at university stood him in good stead. Learning fast with a Lotus 69 in 1972 and realising that he was entering a level where he was competing against much greater technical resources and experience, Byrne sold up and moved to England where those resources lay.

Byrne's fast climb through the ranks of single-seater racing to become Chief Designer of Toleman's Formula 1 team in 1981 came about because of an obvious talent that could be spotted by the people who recruited and pro-

moted him to ever greater responsibility. And Byrne was quick to grasp opportunities when they appeared. In 1980, Toleman had run away with the Formula 2 Championship, and that convinced the team that Formula 1 would be easy. Instead, the team found itself floundering in the top category. Its partners Brian Hart (engine) and Pirelli (tyres) were also new to Formula 1, and the first year was a learning experience for all those involved. Byrne recalls: "The TG280 gave us first and second in the championship and led us to believe we were ready to move on into Formula 1. In fact we had

been lucky—I exploited a loophole in the regulations in which the height of the edges of the bodywork was defined relative to the driver's backside. So I lowered him through the seat and well into the bottom of the monocoque, reducing the ground clearance at the sides of the car by around 15 to 20mm in the process. By the time everyone else had caught on, the Pirelli tyres were developed to a stage where they were superior, and it really was all too easy. It lulled us into a false sense of security. When we arrived in Formula 1, we were in for a massive shock."

Byrne, the most successful Formula 1 car designer in recent years, does not often appear in public, preferring to concentrate his time at the factory. Apart from new car launches, he only attends races at Imola and Monza, both just down the road from Maranello.

Byrne was undaunted by those circumstances and used the opportunity to learn about the technologies and to experiment with suspension and aerodynamics ideas of his own. People in Formula 1 started to take notice of the unassuming designer from South Africa when a young Ayrton Senna demonstrated just what his cars were capable of during 1984. During the Toleman years, Byrne produced the cars that were his best and his worst. Today, the super-light TG185 means the most to him, particularly the satisfaction of doing his first CFRP (carbon-fibre-reinforced plastic) monocoque. He would much prefer to forget the unsuccessful TG181, with its new-to-Formula-1 designer and team, Pirelli tyres, and turbocharged Hart engine, and the pain that accompanied it; they started the season five seconds slower than anyone else, but they learned well. Byrne may be best remembered during that period for his relentless quest for an aerodynamic advantage, however small, and for the common sight of him measuring the track temperature every session, way before most people realised its influence on tyre grip.

Benetton bought the team in 1985 and started the long haul to their two World Championships with Michael Schumacher in 1994 and 1995. Byrne was chief designer during that period, except for a brief sojourn at Reynard, where he designed its stillborn Formula 1 car in 1991. When he returned, he started the association with Ross Brawn that has been so successful in Formula 1.

Byrne's cars are seldom ordinary; he is not afraid to explore new concepts and approaches. Today, rigorous modelling, analysis, and testing back them up, but in the early days he had only his instincts and innate understanding of aerodynamics and tyre/suspension characteristics to rely on.

He says; "With computer aided engineering, such as CFD [computational fluid dynamics] and FEA [finite element analysis], it is hard to keep fully abreast of the very latest methods. I provide the practical experience and overview to guide the use of these super-powerful tools and the specialists who operate them.

"At the end of the day, I still get the same enjoyment out of this new role. The last time I actually engineered a car at the track was in 1993, and I seldom go to races now as there is so much support and research work to do here at the factory. These days, with data transfer via satellite links and modern communications, it is not so necessary." Byrne believes it is more efficient for him to remain at work in Maranello. The same holds for tests, which he describes as "mostly reliability running, which has no direct relevance to performance but does determine success at races."

"It is now so competitive and the pressures have increased," he continues. "The opportunity to innovate has reduced because of the changes in the technical regulations. In the past, my ideas have given us an advantage in some areas, but to be honest, they have hurt reliability. Now Ross has structured things so well, with lots of systems and checks, that the fact that we are generally so reliable is no accident.

"The way Formula 1 is going will reduce the scope for lots of individuality. Take aerodynamics, for instance. There are several aerodynamicists working on it, and we currently have teams shifting the wind tunnel work around the clock. I'm not the only one any more who has new ideas. What I try to do is to make sure there is a balance, and try and prioritise things—that's what it is all about now. My role has definitely changed, but it is still a challenge, just a different one.

"CAD [computer aided design] and CAE [computer aided engineering] have brought about change too. Personally I'm not really computer literate, though I use them. It has been a gradual change, and I have grown to like it for how much more one can do. The scope is enormous, and I wouldn't want to go back. I even find management a challenge!"

Where Ferrari has possibly gained an advantage over

McLaren and Williams is, Byrne believes, not so much in the magnitude of its resources and the fact that engine and chassis are developed on the same site, but in having a different focus for those resources. An intensely competitive nature has led him to push to the limits with every new design, exploiting the very edges of the technical regulations, as written. The successes of Byrne's cars have led to occasional accusations of deliberately overstepping the regulations, and such accusations deeply upset him. Now that the regulations have eliminated many of the control software areas that encouraged doubts, Byrne trusts that his past cars will be judged on the continued competitiveness of their successors. This was born out in 2001, when traction control was allowed back and Ferrari increased its competitiveness.

Ferrari is a large, somewhat spread-out organisation, and Byrne is renowned for the way he almost runs from place to place within it. He typically works fourteen hours a day and often seven days a week, avoiding spending valuable time travelling to races except the local ones at Monza and Imola. Those who hope that Ferrari will become fat with success and start to lose the determination to win are misjudging the people there. Byrne believes that the worst thing they can do is to become complacent and underestimate their opposition. If the team does not push at all times to stay on top, the fall will come quickly, and the climb back will be long and hard.

Byrne says: "I like winning but it is not quite as important as being competitive. You know, being uncompetitive is something I simply can't handle. Losing a race by a few tenths is not so bad; it's down to the details on the day. Coming second, a lap down, is terrible."

Winning makes all the hard work easier and provides an "extra buzz" of motivation to the entire team, Byrne says. "There's not been a day since I started when I've not got out of bed raring to go—raring to get into the office. We've gone through some bad patches, and even then I can honestly say that I've always got into my car really keen to get into work. So from a job satisfaction and personal motivation point of view, I think it's fabulous, but it's up to the individual and not everyone sees it the same way as I do."

Byrne is one of those rare individuals who is at peace with what he is doing. Whether that has come from his upbringing (he credits his father for teaching him how to gain the right balance in life) or from following an enthusiasm and turning it—through hard work and commitment—into a successful career is impossible to tell. He regrets taking so long to realise what he really wanted to do with his life and blames the wasted years on not taking time off before going to university to find that out.

Self-taught, self-motivated, but in no way self-satisfied, Byrne gives the impression that he understands himself as well as he understands a Formula 1 car. He is reluctant to criticise others, though he is generous with praise for those he truly admires, and yet he is prepared to discuss his own faults and limitations as he sees them. He is also happy to give credit to those who have helped or been instrumental in some way in his career. A pure racer who has adapted to the relentless march of technology, Byrne possesses qualities that are unfortunately all too rare in the top ranks of motorsport today.

Although each of Byrne's cars that has won a Formula 1 World Championship has had Michael Schumacher at the wheel, his greatest satisfaction came from winning the Manufacturers' World Championship in 1999, after Schumacher was injured at Silverstone. The cars eventually won without Schumacher. Byrne explains, "That was personally very satisfying, on a level with winning the model glider World Championship, when it was just down to me."

1999 and the Ferrari F399 proved to the world that Ferrari could again win World Championships. Schumacher was on track to win the Drivers' Championship when he broke his leg in an accident at Silverstone. In Malaysia, he returned to the cockpit to completely control the race, gifting a win to Eddie Irvine, (shown here). After the race, the Ferraris were deemed illegal for a tiny bodywork infringement, but regained their points at the FIA International Court of Appeal and took the Manufacturers' Championship in Japan.

3

Design and Build

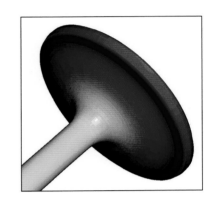

W hen Luca di Montezemolo became President of Ferrari S.p.A in 1992, he took charge of a Scuderia that was at one of the lowest ebbs in its history and took the first step towards building a new racing organisation by appointing Jean Todt as Team Principal of Scuderia Ferrari, with full responsibility for the Formula 1 programme. What Todt found at Maranello did not fill him with confidence; the people and the facilities were there, but they were not being used effectively. The systems, checks, and methodology that

he had installed at Peugeot so effectively were absent. The large workforce had so little focus that its valiant efforts were dissipated in all directions, and the blame for failure was publicly being laid at any door available. Todt had to draw on all the management expertise he had gained while leading Peugeot Sport in the previous eleven years.

What was most lacking was technical leadership. Harvey Postlethwaite was ending his tenure at Ferrari and moving to Tyrrell, and John Barnard was persuaded back to lead chassis design, but the arrangement whereby he based himself and the design department in the United Kingdom, while manufacture, development, and racing were based in Italy was never going to be the answer. Paolo Martinelli

was put in charge of the engine department as it made the transition from V-12s to V-10s for 1996.

ORGANISATION.

Todt soon realised that without the right people in the key technical positions, success would not be possible. There are very few designers and engineers with the proven capability of regularly winning championships. McLaren was just entering its post-Honda loss of form, and Williams, with its engine partner Renault, was in the ascendancy. Coming up fast on the inside was Benetton's unproven combination of driver and engineers, Michael Schumacher, Ross Brawn, and Rory Byrne. When they took the World Championship from

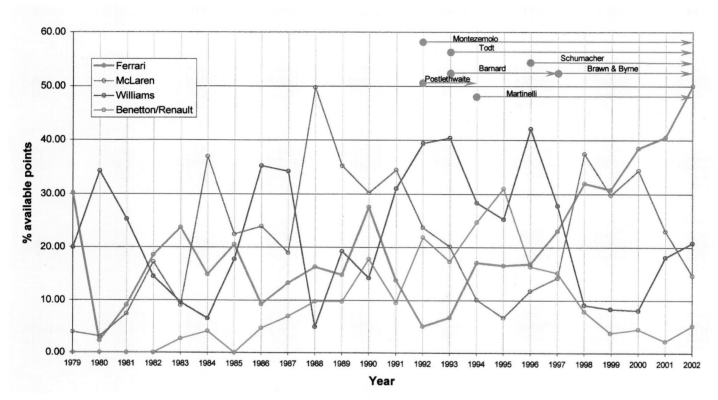

Williams in 1994 and 1995, Todt knew whom he wanted. With Schumacher in place for 1996, it only took that year to persuade Brawn and Byrne to complete the team, with Brawn as Technical Director and Byrne as Chief Designer of the car. Martinelli's V-10s were the equal of the opposition, and Schumacher started to deliver results. Williams' fortunes entered a downturn when Renault withdrew from Formula 1 at the end of 1996, and McLaren started to rise again with Mercedes' involvement and Mika Hakkinen's increasing maturity as a driver. From 1998 to 2000, the World Championship was a straight fight between Ferrari and McLaren, Schumacher and Hakkinen, apart from the second half of 1999 after Schumacher's crash at Silverstone. The accident left Schumacher with a broken leg, and he missed the next six races as a consequence. After Silverstone, Eddie Irvine carried Ferrari's challenge forward.

In 1999, they won the Manufacturers' Championship and would probably have taken the Drivers' Championship, too, if Schumacher had not been injured. Schumacher was able to return for the last two races and assist Irvine's championship battle with Hakkinen, which Irvine only lost in the final race in Japan.

When Brawn and Byrne arrived at the end of 1996 and beginning of 1997, respectively, they inherited John Barnard's F310 but no chassis design department, as all work in this area had been carried out in the U.K., and the staff at Maranello had been moved to other areas. For 1997, an extensively rebodied F310B benefited from Byrne's aerodynamic input, and a Mark 2 version of the 046 engine was used. Meanwhile, Brawn set about creating a chassis department virtually from scratch.

Brawn considers '97, '98, and '99 to have been catch-up

LEFT: *[Fig. 3-3] The Manufacturers' World Championship points. Ferrari's improvement since 1993 is evident and significantly more prolonged than any other recovery by its main competitors.*

RIGHT: *Ross Brawn, Technical Director, and Paolo Martinelli, Director of Engines, head the Scuderia's technical organisation that created the Ferrari F1-2000, reporting to Jean Todt, Team Principal.*

years, where they arrived at the first race of each year to discover they were half a second or more off the pace. They relied on Schumacher to be competitive, though in each year they steadily improved to end the seasons close to McLaren. It was only in 2000 that they felt they had a car that was truly competitive at enough of the circuits to really achieve their goal of winning both championships. The first race in Melbourne confirmed this with a one-two finish for Schumacher and Barrichello. The strength and quality of the organisation that Todt, Brawn, Byrne, and Martinelli have created can best be judged by Ferrari's performance in the World Championship, from the low point in the early '90s to today. In 2002, Ferrari

scored 50 percent of all the points available (first and second in every race would only yield 61.5 percent of the points); at no time in the previous 30 years has such a steady rise in performance been seen in Formula 1 (Figure 3-3).

The technical organisation that created the Ferrari F1-2000 is shown at left. Jean Todt, as Team Principal, has the overall responsibility for the Scuderia's activities, including technical aspects, logistics, sponsorship, public and press relations, and administration. Ross Brawn, Technical Director, and Paolo Martinelli, Director of Engines, both report directly to Todt. Brawn has overall responsibility for the whole car and for manufacturing, which is an unusual area for a Technical Director to take on. Martinelli has overall control of the engine programmes, while Brawn has the additional role of being responsible for all activities at the track. They also share a number of specialist departments. Rory Byrne, Head of Vehicle Planning, directs all the vehicle programmes and reports to Brawn. Byrne controls chassis and gearbox design, aerodynamics, vehicle dynamics analysis, and structures. Research and Development, under Giorgio Ascanelli, reports to Brawn, as does Manufacturing under Mario Almondo. The race team is managed by Stefano Domenicali, and the Chief Mechanic is Nigel Stepney, who also has responsibility for the race shop, reporting on all technical matters to Brawn.

PROGRAMME.

As soon as a new engine or car runs and the qualities and deficiencies of the new design can be assessed, team members' thoughts turn to the next one.

Figure 3-5 on the following page illustrates the scheduling of the main parts of a new car. Engine concept work starts in January, as soon as dynamometer testing is well under way on the engine to be raced that year. New car work starts in earnest as soon as the race season is under way in March.

Ross Brawn describes the process: "When we get back from the initial races of the new car, and we have seen how it compares with the new cars of our competitors, we sit down and start the process of specifying next year's car. From around April, we then have a new car meeting every two weeks throughout the season, which starts with just a small number of people—Paolo and Rory, of course—and gradually expands as design, analysis, and R&D people come in on the discussions.

"We try to analyse the strengths and weaknesses of our car relative to competitors and determine what changes, either to the overall performance of some aspect, or the compromises we have to make. For instance, we decide on fuel tank size, and the resulting wheelbase, and pitch and yaw inertias fairly early on, and try to come up with a configuration that works best on the greatest number of tracks. The trend has been towards larger and larger fuel tanks, to enable the driver to run the longest possible first stint, but that leads to a longer wheel base and the displacement of heavy components away from the centre of gravity [C of G], to make space for the fuel."

Ferrari has found that pitch motion (about the horizontal transverse axis through the C of G) and yaw motion (about the vertical axis through the C of G) are both important aspects of car performance, and as the inertias about these axes both increase with wheelbase, they are affected by fuel tank size. In particular, the vehicle dynamics department has found that the car is sensitive to the pitch inertia effects, as well as the more obvious yaw inertia. It has run extensive analysis on the trade-off for all circuits, and tank size has been chosen on the information gleaned, as well as from race strategy considerations. It is in making decisions such as this that Ross Brawn excels, where overall race performance, on average more than seventeen circuits, is a function of different factors, involving different disciplines.

Activity	January	February	March	April	May	June	July	August	Sept.	Oct.	Nov.	Dec.	January	February	March
Car launch														7th Feb.	
First Race															12th March
Engine:															
Study & modelling															
Design															
Detail and FEA															
Large castings															
Machining															
Assembly															
Dyno. testing															
Track testing															
Race															
Gearbox:															
Study & modelling															
Case definition															
Spacer definition															
Hydraulic definition															
Design															
Manufacture															
Assembly															
Rig testing															
Track testing															
Race															
Car:															
Monocoque:															
Study & modelling															
Define															
Design															
Manufacture															
Roll hoop - aero															
- design															
- manufacture															
FIA tests															
Body & wings:															
Study & modelling															
Aero definition:															
Design															
Manufacture															
Suspension:															
Study & modelling															
Aero definition:															
Design															
Manufacture															
Systems															
Study & modelling															
Design															
Manufacture															
Rig testing															
Track testing															
Race															

Brawn says: "We set targets for weight reduction as we want to put as much ballast low down in the car as possible and to be able to move it around to tune the car. We decide on the areas where a particular weight reduction is possible and may then run lighter components during the season to check for reliability and be able to confirm those parts of the design.

"Tyre degradation is always an issue, and we shall do considerable analysis to identify areas where increasing camber and toe stiffness, for instance, can reduce degradation.

"We try not to involve Rory in day-to-day racing and the reliability issues it inevitably throws up, so that he can get on with the new car. He is tracking the output from three shifts in the wind tunnel, as well as directing the design of the chassis and transmission. The longer the aero-

ABOVE: *[Fig. 3-5] The schedule to research, design, build, test, and prepare a Formula 1 car for the first race varies little each year. The amount of work, however, increases steadily for a team such as Ferrari.*

RIGHT: *Stress analysis of the Tipo 049 connecting rod little end. The greatest stress is in the blue areas, the least in the yellow, according to the scale.*

"We set targets for weight reduction as we want to put as much ballast low down in the car as possible and to be able to move it around to tune the car."

dynamicists can spend in the tunnel before the design is frozen, generally the greater the gains they come up with. The monocoque pattern must be started around August, but Rory may come to a meeting with a request for another couple of weeks to achieve a significant gain, and I have to see how things can be shuffled to give him the extra time. The planning department has to interleave the changing requirements of both engine and chassis build and see how critical facilities can be rescheduled."

The schedule in Figure 3-5 does not start to illustrate the complexity of the planning required to design and build a small batch of Formula 1 cars in just twelve months, while at the same time developing and supplying the racing department with components for the current car. Even a team with the funding and facilities of Ferrari has limitations on its resources. The loading of designers and their CAD and CAM (computer aided manufacturing) facilities; CFD, FEA,

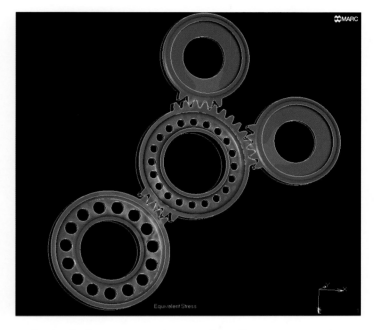

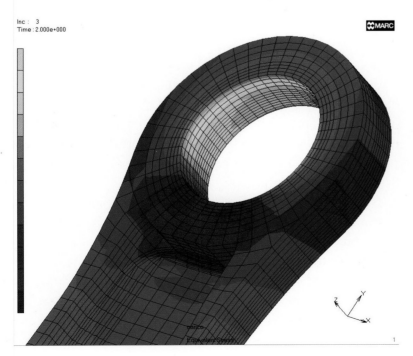

and vehicle dynamics analysts and workstations; rapid prototyping machines; the foundry, machine shop, and composites departments; rig shops; wind tunnels; dynamometers; and even the track test programmes must all be planned in minute detail and in such a way that it is also flexible enough to respond to the unexpected. Ferrari has recently built a large logistics centre alongside the Fiorano test track, to handle the preparation, storage, and transportation needs of the race and test teams.

Ferrari works closely with its technical partners, integrating them more closely into the design and development process than perhaps any other Formula 1 team. This close involvement of outside companies inevitably leads to the need for many meetings, often involving time-consuming overseas travel by key personnel. As the relationships strengthen and become closer, a process brought about by mutual success more than anything else, the exchange of data expands. Race strategies depend on information and decisions made jointly, and Ferrari's technical partners are an integral part of the planning and execution of races.

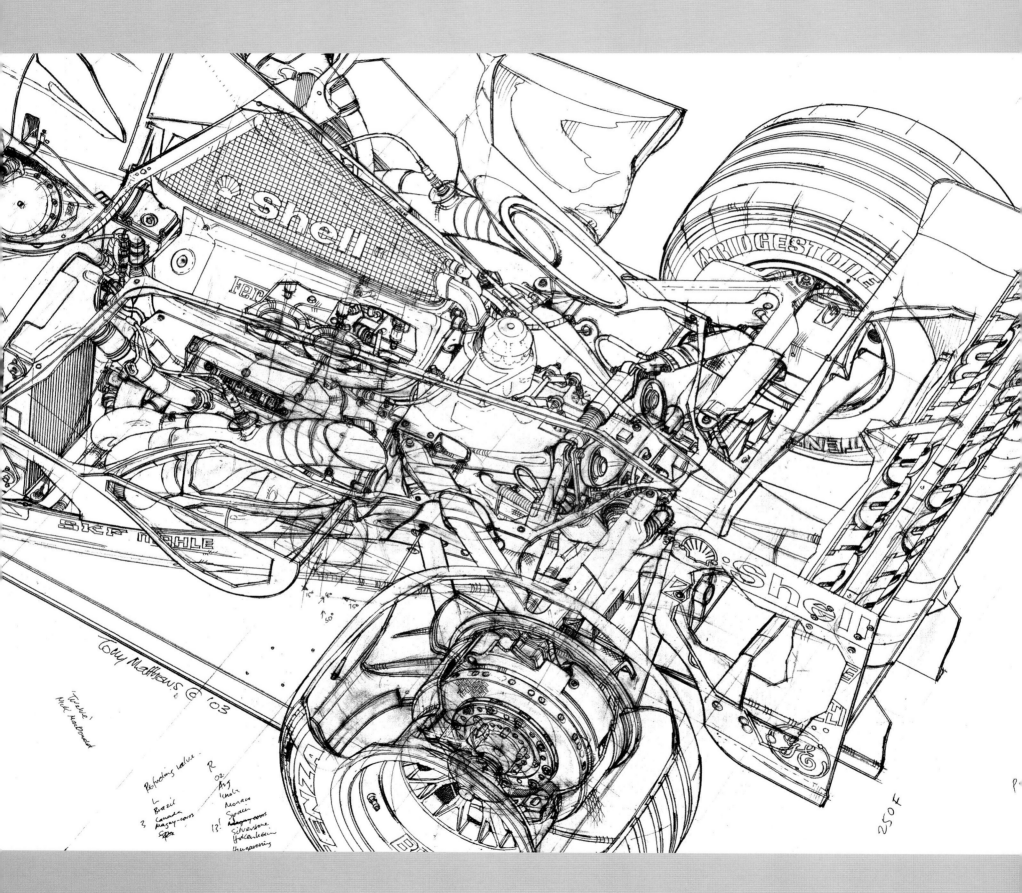

4

Car

*T*he layout and shape of current Formula 1 cars are greatly influenced by two factors: the FIA Formula 1 Technical Regulations and aerodynamics. This is why all current cars look very similar, both with the body on and without it, distinguished mainly by the diverse exterior colour schemes dictated by their sponsors. The technical regulations constrain design to control the performance of the cars and to ensure an adequate level of protection for the driver. There is the additional aim of controlling costs, not the cost of manufacturing

the components—technical regulations have little bearing on how much teams are prepared to spend on making parts—but on research into technologies that may be employed. Teams have agreed by consensus that there are certain technologies that should be banned or restricted to prevent all chassis, engine, tyre, and fuel manufacturers from having to rush headlong after new and expensive R&D goals, many of them irrelevant to the prime automobile businesses in which most of the manufacturers are involved.

Within the constraints imposed by the FIA, the pursuit of improvements has never been more intense or more costly. Teams focus on five key performance parameters—power, weight, downforce, drag, and tyre performance—and

the technologies that determine how much of that potential performance can be delivered by the driver. These technologies include centre of gravity (C of G) position, suspension kinematics, transient aerodynamics, engine driveability, brake performance, gear-change, and other various control system characteristics. In the past twenty years, the computer has come to the aid of designers and engineers, enabling human understanding of a racing car to move from the realm of black art to science.

When studying a modern Formula 1 car such as the Ferrari F1-2000, it is worth bearing in mind the designers' constraints and to be aware of the objectives they have while working to extract the maximum performance from a design

that is within the regulations.

ENGINE: The maximum power output of the engine is constrained by controlling the engine cycle (normally aspirated, four-stroke piston engine), swept volume (3 litres), number of pistons (ten) and valves (four per cylinder), and fuel (pump petrol). The route to more power is increasing rpm, but not at the expense of worse volumetric, thermal, or mechanical efficiency. Some limits have been placed on rpm by regulations constraining certain materials in certain applications, for example; crankshafts and camshafts must be steel or iron and may not be made of composite materials.

Equally important aspects of engine design are the weight, size, and C of G height, all of which affect the overall car characteristics. Shorter stroke not only permits higher rpm due to reduced inertia loads, but also lowers the crankshaft to lower the masses in the engine. As the bore increases to compensate, the combustion engineers must deal with the worse and worse combustion chamber shape, as it becomes a larger and thinner disc.

Absolute maximum power is of little benefit on today's Grand Prix circuits if it is not controllable by the driver. Computer control of the throttles, ignition timing, fuel delivery, and induction resonant tuning, via the moveable trumpets, are all employed to smooth the torque curve and tame the more than 800 bhp available.

One of the oldest truisms in motor racing is "In order to finish first, you must first finish." The minimum requirement for a Formula 1 engine is that it should survive and deliver its full design power throughout the Sunday of a Grand Prix event. This requires a life of around 350km. So essential is this that rig, dynamometer, and track testing have become major activities and major expenditures. Ferrari builds around 400 engines each year (plus another 100 for each customer team) for R&D, reliability and development testing, and racing.

TRANSMISSION: The development of semiautomatic and automatic gear changing and the ability of the driver to keep his hands on the wheel while commanding gear changes that do not require him to take precautions to avoid over-revving the engine have permitted an increase in the number of ratios available to him. The regulations limit the number to seven, with a minimum of four, to effectively ban CVTs (continuously variable transmissions), and it is now normal to use the maximum number permitted in a trade-off between the number of gear changes necessary and the torque curve and maximum power of the engine.

The transmission is a large mass, situated far back in the car, contributing to the yaw and pitch inertia as well as affecting the critical aerodynamics of the diffuser and internal airflow exiting from the radiators. The pressure to make the transmission smaller and lighter has to be balanced against reliability. It is full of hot rotating components, subject to repeated shock loading during gear changes and as the car is driven over kerbs, and it suffers also from having a complex electro-hydraulic system to control the clutch, gear

The cutaway drawing of the Ferrari F1-2000.

change, and limited-slip differential.

CHASSIS: The size and strength of the chassis, particularly the monocoque, are determined more by the need to pass the FIA's ever more stringent safety tests than by vehicle dynamic requirements. Designing a structure that will pass the dynamic and static crash tests and that adheres to the minimum dimensions laid down in the technical regulations results in a monocoque that is stiff enough to act as an adequate connection between the front and rear suspensions. The two main features that the designer must decide upon early in the programme are the size of the fuel tank, based on the team's racing strategies as developed in previous years, and the height of the nose and the forward part of the monocoque that encloses the driver's legs. CFD analysis and wind tunnel testing will determine this latter feature.

So stiff are current CFRP monocoques that the overall torsional and bending stiffness, axle to axle, is governed by the critical joints at the front of the engine to the back of fuel tank, and the engine to the gearbox. The engine and gearbox have both reduced in cross section as they have been developed and run at 100 to 150°C. Careful choice of main case materials, expansion of the cross section at the critical joint

faces, and close dialogue between the various design departments involved are all important.

The weight of the car, checked at any time as the car enters the pits, must not be less than 600kg. It is possible to design a current Formula 1 car to weigh in, including an 80kg driver, at considerably less than that figure. The reason that so much effort and manufacturing expense are concentrated on reducing the weight of components, then ballasting with around 70kg of tungsten, is mainly due to the fact that designers wish to achieve the lowest possible C of G. On current cars the tyres are too small, and the track width is too narrow—both limited by the technical regulations—and lowering the C of G has a significant decrease on the somewhat overloaded tyres. Additionally, to be able to adjust the fore and aft weight distribution, particularly as the normal layout of components does not naturally result in the ideal weight on each axle, is a major benefit.

In spite of the minimum weight limit, originally imposed to ensure that components were built strong enough and to discourage excessively costly weight reduction, it is now necessary to put limits on some of the materials used in particular applications. The primary structure of the car is

LEFT: *The layout of the principal components of the F1-2000 are shown in the CAD general arrangement drawing.*

RIGHT: *[Fig. 4-5] Tungsten ballast is distributed throughout the length of the undertray to maintain the C of G as low as possible and to adjust the weight distribution. The yellow "T" is a Kevlar cover for part of the chassis wiring loom—a heavy item, which is also mounted as low as possible.*

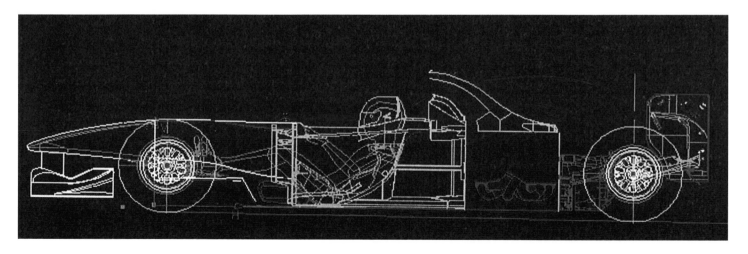

CFRP, as is the suspension, any low-temperature parts of the engine and transmission, and all unstressed covers. Aluminium castings are used for the hot non-highly stressed parts, but in some areas, such as the gear case, are being replaced by fabricated or investment-cast titanium. Steel is still the material used for hot rotating parts. To discourage the expensive development of fibre-reinforced composites and alloys for wheels, crankshaft, and so on, limits are imposed on their use.

The grooved tyres mandated are limited to widths of 355mm at the front and 380mm at the rear. These dimensions, along with the same maximum diameter front and rear, lead to a possible tyre footprint width distribution of 48/52 percent if the maximum potential tyre width is used. The natural weight distribution is in the low 40 percent region, and so the 70kg of ballast made available by designing the car well below the weight limit is used to adjust the weight distribution toward the higher 40 percent range (Figures 4-5 and 4-6 on the following page). Too much weight on the front will harm traction, and so on traction-critical circuits, such as Monaco, the weight will be kept toward the rear and less-than-maximum-width front tyres may be used.

The limitation in tyre width allied with the narrow track (limited to just more than 1.4m by the overall width regulation) leads to greater tyre load sensitivity and a loss of tyre performance due to lateral load transfer during cornering. Lowering the C of G is just about the only way to minimise these effects. The greatest weight-reduction exercises are applied to the engine and transmission, as these masses are behind the C of G, and so any weight removed can be added as ballast ahead of the C of G. The heaviest parts of these two components are rotating, some very fast, and so their inertias must be added to the total to be accelerated.

SUSPENSION: Suspension requirements—appropriate

kinematic characteristics, that is, the way the suspension characteristics vary with vertical movement to suit the tyres and chassis dynamics, minimum unsprung mass, adequate stiffness, and minimum aerodynamic disturbance—have not changed for many years. Packaging the components as low in the chassis as possible must be balanced against accessibility and structural integrity. The insight into suspension possibilities afforded by the brief development of active suspension systems in the late '80s and early '90s (before they were banned) has led to the stiffness and damping of the vertical and roll modes being partially decoupled. The addition of a third spring and/or damper linking the two sides provides increased vertical rate without contributing to roll.

The two arts of suspension design and tuning have always been to match the suspension characteristics to the tyres and minimise the disturbance due to bumps. Now, with the development of simulation technologies, sophisticated rigs, and stiff lightweight, structures, it has become a science. Tyres are the last to yield to the computer's analysis powers, with non-isotropic material properties and high strain rates taking FEA analysis to extremes of complexity. Validation of tyre performance on rigs and on the track is still one of the greatest challenges and, of course, one of the keys to overall performance.

BRAKES: The brake system is by far the most powerful system on a Formula 1 car, absorbing more than 2,000 horsepower when the brakes are used to stop the car from maximum speed. Maximum diameter and thickness of the carbon-carbon brake discs and single six-piston calipers imposed by the regulations limit the area of the friction surface and the thermal capacity of the brakes. Certain circuits, such as Montreal and Imola, push cars to the limit of brake wear. Providing adequate cooling without compromising the aerodynamics around the front wheels is critical to the brakes surviving a race distance.

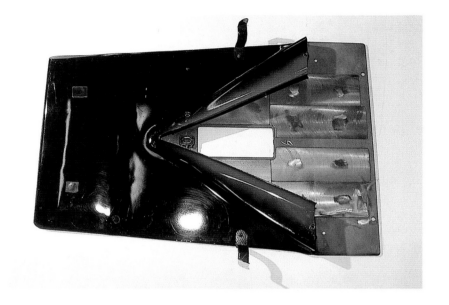

The stiffness of the brake circuits determines the maximum force the driver is able to apply to the pads before running out of pedal stroke. While the pedal and master cylinder installation and the hydraulic circuit all contribute, it is caliper stiffness that dominates. After Formula 1's flirtation with metal matrix composite alloys (MMC) and aluminium-beryllium for calipers, FIA imposed a modulus of elasticity limit of 80Gpa on the material used in calipers. Materials to the limits of this stiffness have been developed and caliper design has been refined with FEA.

Brake balance, front to rear, has a major influence on the stability of any car under hard braking. Many racing drivers like to brake deep into a corner, turning in on the brakes and modulating them to control the yaw rate of the car. Michael Schumacher is one of them, and he has gained a reputation as a driver who is able to exploit a less stable car better than others. However, to do so without overstepping the mark and losing control under braking requires that the brake balance be set up precisely for all combinations of speed and brake effort. For many years, racing cars have had

ABOVE: [Fig. 4-6] The tungsten ballast also fills the splitter plate at the front of the undertray.

RIGHT: The rear half of the chassis structure is composed of the engine and transmission, carrying all the loads from the rear suspension.

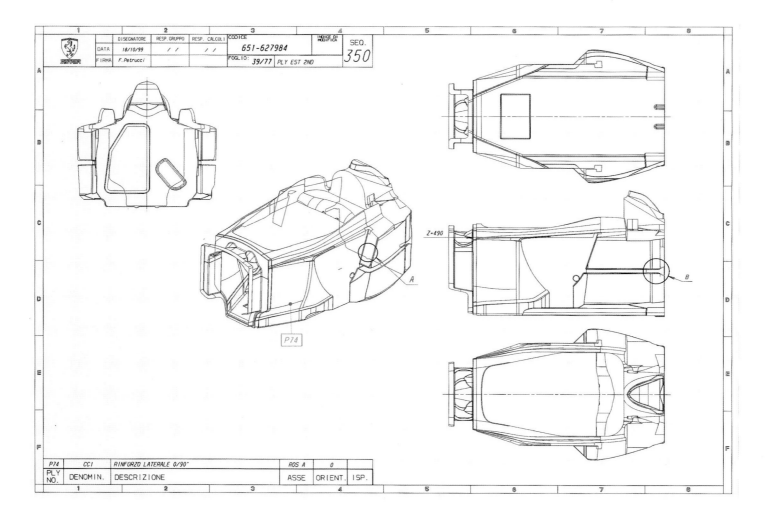

a mechanical adjustment of the brake balance to allow drivers to compensate for changes in fuel load, track conditions, and tyre wear. Some used this control to alter the balance corner to corner, but it is distracting to have to keep track of brake balance on a mechanical system. In 2000, it was permitted to have an electro-hydraulic balance actuation system, which allowed the driver to control the brake balance at the touch of a button on the steering wheel. This has since been banned. The Ferrari F1-2000 is fitted with such a system, and Schumacher exploited it to the full to fine-tune the handling of the car under braking and on entry into each corner. **AERODYNAMICS:** Ever since Chaparral demonstrated in the 1960s that aerodynamic downforce has as much of an influence on overall performance as drag, Formula 1 designers have been pursuing the holy grail of generating as much downforce for as little drag as is possible. Running triple shifts in one or more multimillion dollar wind tunnels, combined with teams of graduate aerodynamicists working to improve the accuracy of CFD analysis, currently constitutes the biggest R&D effort in the development of Formula 1 cars.

Ground effect aerodynamics are potentially so powerful that if they were not regulated, the cars would by now be generating g-forces in excess of human tolerance. Successive regulations to curb the magnitude of the downforce that can be created have just about kept pace with development, such that the maximum g-levels attainable are around 5 g, with

LEFT: *The drawing of the monocoque shows the positioning of just one layer of 0 degree/90 degree pre-preg CFRP reinforcement that goes into the lay-up of the structure.*

RIGHT: *The electro–hydraulic power steering takes its input from steering column torque, measured by strain gauges mounted on the column.*

"Ground effect aerodynamics are potentially so powerful that if they were not regulated, the cars would by now be generating g-forces in excess of human tolerance."

tyres that have peak coefficients of friction in excess of 2.0; that is, the downforce is more than 1.5 times the weight of the car at the maximum cornering speeds of 260+kph. The drag of a Formula 1 car is high, limiting the top speed to around 300 to 350kph, depending upon whether it is set up for maximum downforce or minimum drag, in spite of its 800+bhp.

Open-wheel racing car aerodynamics are not only about

optimising the three main downforce-generating areas: the front wing, working in ground effect; the undertray and rear diffuser, also working in ground effect; and the rear wing, which interacts with the diffuser. It is just as much about minimising or exploiting positively the parts of the car that detract from the main objective of maximising the lift/drag ratio. These include the tip vortices trailing from the front wing tips, which, combined with the vortices shed by the front wheels, interact strongly with the cooling and undertray; the need to pass air through various cooling radiators and to the brakes; the open cockpit and driver's head, which combine to reduce the pressure recovery in the ram intake to the engine; the exhaust efflux, which interacts with the rear wing; the rear wheels; and the hot radiator exit air that flows through the body and exits into the base region, affecting the rear diffuser and rear wing. Ensuring that all these components work together and exhibit the desired dynamic characteristics as the car heaves, pitches, rolls, and yaws in close proximity to the ground is still primarily an experimental technique, in spite of the enormous advances made with CFD. Simulating the car in a wind tunnel requires expensive models, accurate flow simulation, thousands of test parts, and hours and hours of semi-automated tunnel testing with its associated data acquisition and analysis.

TYRES: Tyres (along with fuels and lubricants) have always been supplied by a contracted company, never developed by a Formula 1 team itself. Technical communication was limited for a long time to the tyre supplier providing a monitoring service when the car was being tested or raced, the supplier itself needing the information to develop and select the most suitable tyre for a given circuit. Limited data concerning the tyre characteristics was supplied, based on rig testing. As teams began to make computer simulations of vehicle dynamics, better data was demanded, and the limitations of rig testing soon became apparent. As the engine and

aerodynamics have become more and more refined within the regulations and the yearly improvements have become smaller, integration of the tyres with the chassis has increased in priority as the area of development that has the greatest potential for gains in performance.

In 2000, Bridgestone was the sole tyre supplier in Formula 1. In an informal agreement with the FIA, Bridgestone agreed to supply the whole grid with tyres that had reasonably hard compounds, as a means of controlling performance. Bridgestone was happy to do this, as conservative compounds are unlikely to cause wear or blistering problems, and it was a preferred approach compared to adding more grooves to the tyres. Toward the end of the year, having announced its intention to compete from 2001, Michelin started to contract teams, leading Bridgestone to start being less conservative in preparation for the coming tyre war. Developing tyres for more than one design of car inevitably results in a compromise, and thus it is of utmost importance for a team to become the prime customer of its chosen tyre supplier, to ensure the maximum influence on tyre development. Winning is a good strategy for persuading a tyre manufacturer to work closely with a team, and Ferrari has succeeded in forming a very close relationship with Bridgestone since 2000.

Data, the tools to gather it accurately, and validated simulations are the keys to chassis/tyre development. While static loads and suspension geometry effects can be simulated in a tyre test dynamometer, dynamic loading, kinematic geometry effects, real track surfaces with varying degrees of rubber laid down by similar and competing tyres, and track and air temperature variations cannot. The only way to measure actual tyre characteristics, on a given track and on a given day, is to turn the car into a tyre dynamometer. To do so, the car must be extensively instrumented to measure tyre attitude and loads. For such costly R&D to be effective

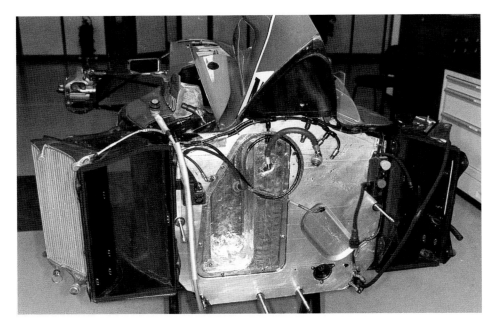

requires a degree of cooperation and trust (with each other's data) that can emerge only from long-term commitment between supplier and team. Such partnerships are now being formed and will undoubtedly be the basis of significant performance gains.

The Formula 1 Sporting Regulations control the number and types of tyre that can be used during an event. In 2000, a maximum of thirty-two dry tyres and twenty-eight wet tyres were available to each driver. Two possible specifications of dry tyre were available, of which the driver had to select one specification for use in qualifying and the race. Without competition that year, Bridgestone did not have to take risks with construction or compound selection, basing its choices on previous years. However, with Michelin as a competitor, the prediction of track state, weather, car set-up, and their teams' strategies all become crucial in determining the choice of just two tyre specifications to cover their contracted cars. The accuracy with which that choice is made is likely to influence, and may even determine, the results of the race.

ABOVE: *The rear of the monocoque is recessed for the oil tank. The mechanical fuel pump is inside the fuel tank, in the lower right corner, and is driven by a shaft from the front of the engine. Note that the top engine mountings only come halfway up the fuel tank bulkhead.*

RIGHT: *Throttle and brakes pedals, with the CFRP steering column passing between them. There is no clutch pedal. The bottom mounting of the left-side damper can just be seen.*

FUEL AND LUBRICANTS: The relationship between a team and its fuel and lubricant supplier has developed in a similar manner to that with the tyre supplier, but it will be influenced by whether the team develops and manufactures its own engines. In the past, when the fuel regulations have been relatively free, fuel development was an integral part of power development. Now the scope for major power gains is small, but, in order to exploit it, the working relationships must be closer. Trade-offs between power and fuel economy and the influence of lubricants on both power and reliability require as intimate a relationship as that with the tyre supplier.

SYSTEMS: Racing cars have always had systems—cooling, lubrication, fuel, ignition, and electrics—but they did not always have such a major influence on the performance of the car, nor give the designers such great headaches, nor take up as much track test time as they do today. Since the early 1980s—when Formula 1 cars first had computer control of fuel injection, the early active suspension systems, and digital data systems— electronic systems have infiltrated into every corner of the car, limited only by the constantly argued over and re-written regulations.

Albert Einstein is reputed to have once said, "Man has a tendency to believe what he has just measured." Formula 1 engineers started to make measurements on running cars just as soon as the technology became available to acquire reliable data. Now, multiple channels are acquired at high-

data rates, then stored or telemetered to the pits, where data is analysed on banks of computers or beamed via satellites back to the waiting engineers at the factory. Every temperature, pressure, load, and movement on the engine, transmission, suspension, brakes, tyres, and driver is monitored to establish the state of the individual systems at all times.

Measurement is the cornerstone of a control system; the output of the control computer to the actuators is only as good as the measurements. In 2000, certain systems could be controlled in this way, within stringent limitations, and were not considered to be driver aids. They included ignition, fuel injection, drive-by-wire throttles, trumpet length, clutch, gear-change, differential, power steering, and brake balance. Computer control of these systems was regulated in a way that did not detract from the skill of the driver.

To ensure that the regulations were adhered to, the FIA sent teams of software analysts to each Formula 1 team and its suppliers to inspect and certify the codes, line by line. This enormous task tied up team software engineers for days, and yet rumours and unsubstantiated accusations of cheating abounded, bringing the sport into disrepute in the eyes of the public.

From the 2001 Spanish GP onwards, the FIA changed its approach to control system regulation, permitting complete freedom on the engine and transmission, but banning control of all other systems. The inspection procedures still involve some software inspection, but if no actuators are found in a system, it is not being computer controlled. The rumours have ceased.

F1-2000 TECHNICAL SPECIFICATIONS

Car Specifications

Wheelbase	3,075mm
Overall length	4,503mm
Front track	1,457mm
Rear track	1,416mm
Overall width	1,798mm
Overall height	995mm (from ground at nominal static ride height)
Overall height	949mm (from reference plane)
Weight	less than 463kg (without ballast and driver) 600kg (including ballast and driver)
Weight (minimum running)	600kg
Weight distribution range	43 to 45percent on the front
Wheel widths	Front: 330mm (13") dia. x 324mm wide Rear: 330mm (13") dia. x 348mm wide
Ride heights	Front: 14 to 20mm (static ride height range) Rear: 50 to 61mm (static ride height range) Front: 1 to 29mm (maximum suspension travel, excluding tyre) Rear: 1 to 65mm (maximum suspension travel, excluding tyre)

Engine, Tipo 049

Fuel Consumption

Max.	72 litres/100km (Australia and San Marino)
Min.	63 litres/100km (Germany and Italy) (See detailed specification on page 102)
Configuration	90-degree V-10; twin overhead camshafts; 4 valves per cylinder
Capacity	2,997cc
Power	806CV @ 17,500rpm
Peak torque	35Kgm @ 15,500rpm
Weight	less than 106kg, inc. clutch, excl. exhausts

Transmission

Clutch	115mm (4.5") diameter, electrohydraulic (steering wheel paddle controlled), pull-operated, carbon-carbon
Gear box	Seven speeds, longitudinal; machined and fabricated titanium/CFRP
Gear-change	Electro-hydraulic sequential (steering wheel paddle controlled)
Differential	Electro-hydraulically controlled limited-slip, epicyclic
Half-shafts	Steel; tripod joints
Weight	45kg, including hydraulic valve manifold and valves

Monocoque

Weight	44kg (without ballast)
Materials	Carbon-fibre and Kevlar-reinforced epoxy; Hexcell aluminium honeycomb
Tank capacity	144 litres
Torsional stiffness	2497Kgm/deg; monocoque 667Kgm/deg; axle to axle

Suspension and Steering

Springs	Torsion bar, push-rod and lever operated Belville washer third spring (front and rear)
Anti-roll bars	Cantilever springs in bending—(front); lever operated, torsion bar—(rear).
Front wheel rate	16 to 54kg/mm
Rear wheel rate	7 to 20kg/mm
Dampers	Through-rod, push-rod, and rocker operated; non-through-rod third damper (front and rear)—Sachs
Steering	Electronically controlled, hydraulic power assisted, rack and pinion
Uprights	Machined and fabricated titanium
Wishbones and push rods	Carbon-fibre-reinforced epoxy; titanium end fittings; ball joints or flexure pivots

Brakes

Calipers	One per wheel, lithium-aluminium, four-piston—Brembo
Discs and pads	Carbon-carbon; ventilated discs: 278mm diam. max.; 28mm thick, max.—Brembo or Carbon Industries
Balance adjustment	Electro-hydraulic, driver adjustable

Body and Aerodynamic Components

Cooling	Water: two water/air radiators in side pods Engine oil: two oil/air radiators in side pods (left hand combined with transmission oil) Transmission oil: oil/air Hydraulic oil: oil/air Brakes: Air ducts to each disc/caliper
Body and undertray	Carbon-reinforced epoxy; Nomex honeycomb
Wings	Carbon-reinforced epoxy; multi-element

Controls and Instrumentation

Throttle	Drive-by-wire, electro-hydraulic
Brakes	Left-foot operated; driver adjustable balance
Steering wheel	Paddles for gear-change and clutch; multi-function displays and system controls; quick-release removable
Cockpit	Multi-function system controls

Systems

Electrical	12V; 41-amp alternator; 2Ahr battery—Magneti Marelli
Electronics	ECU Step 9—Magneti Marelli. 98 inputs; 45 outputs; 1 HDLC; 1 Ethernet; 5 CAN
Hydraulic	Engine-driven variable displacement pump; sealed system; 200bar; Moog servo valves
Data	Onboard storage; telemetry to pits—Magneti Marelli; Delphi ADR2 accident data recorder
Radio	Two-way voice, digital—Magnetti Marelli

Safety

Survival cell	Minimum dimensions; anti-intrusion side panels
FIA tests	Frontal, side, and rear impact tests; nose push-off, survival cell panel, and roll protection static tests; collapsible steering column impact test.
Driver head protection	Confor cockpit head padding
Wheel tethers	1 per wheel, 50kN breaking load

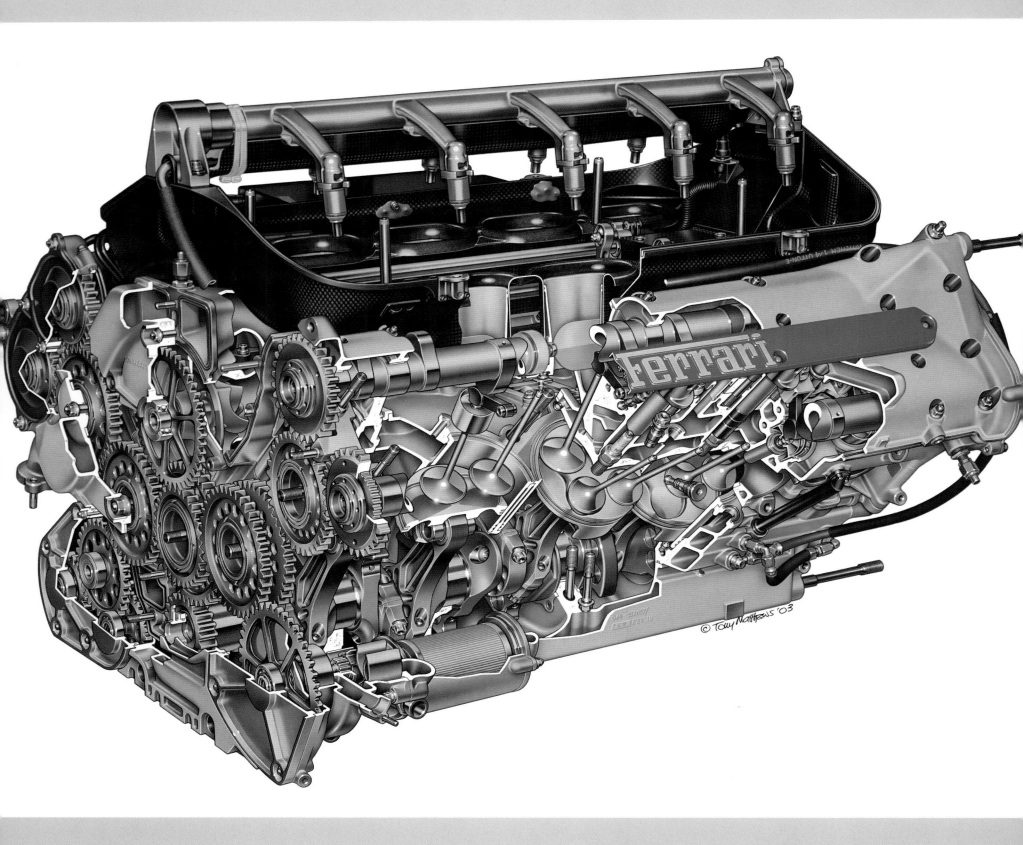

5

Engine

*I*f Ernest Henri, the designer of the 1913 3.0-litre GP Peugeot, were *alive today and able to inspect the 3.0-litre engine of the Ferrari F1-2000, he would be able to instantly comprehend the layout and to identify and understand the functioning of the majority of the mechanical components. That is because the arrangement of the power-producing components has changed little in the eighty-seven years since he designed the cylinder head of the Peugeot engine, with its four valves per cylinder and twin overhead camshafts driven by spur gears,*

which has defined the layout of racing piston engines ever since. He might be perplexed by the V-10 cylinder arrangement, the lack of obvious valve springs, and the amount of electronic monitoring and control. He might also be surprised at the specific output of 268hp/litre, compared to the 31hp/litre of his engine, and the 18,000rpm at which the engine is able to run without destroying itself, compared to the 2,900rpm he achieved. Then again, perhaps he would not, being an engineer of great vision.

In the intervening years, Grand Prix engine designers have been influenced by the technical regulations, R&D carried out to develop aircraft engines during two world wars, and the available and permitted fuels. They have explored various cycles—normally aspirated, supercharged, turbo-charged, and even gas turbine—and a variety of cylinder arrangements. During the last 3.0-litre formula, from 1966 to 1985, before the turbo-charged 1.5-litre proved superior, engine designers started to work with their chassis designer colleagues to optimise the whole system. V-8, V-12, flat-12, and even H-16 configurations were explored, with consensus favouring the V-8 as the best compromise among ultimate power, under-car aerodynamics, and structural stiffness. By the time the formula returned to 3.0-litre normally aspirated engines in 1995, engine designers had converged on the V-10 arrangement, agreeing that it provides as near as possible optimum cylinder size for

combustion and thermal efficiency, with the best compromise of length and cross section for structural properties. This was in spite of the problems of resonant tuning and torsional harmonics that the arrangement gave them. By this time they had sophisticated computer software to assist them in sorting out the problems and electronic control systems to optimise all aspects of operating the engine.

A plot of specific power against calendar year of the GP engines developed by Ferrari (Figures 5-5 and 5-6 on page 90) shows the pace of development since 1948, when Ferrari entered GP racing, and covers the Formula 1 period since. The three engine cycles employed are differentiated, as it would be confusing to use specific power to compare engines that are either supercharged or turbo-charged with ones that are normally aspirated. The reduction in specific output of the turbo in its last year in 1988 is due to the FIA's reduction in permitted boost pressure from no limit to 2.5 bar.

Here are some engine fundamentals to consider. In a normally aspirated engine of a given swept volume and running on a given fuel (the swept volume determines the total mass of oxygen inducted by the engine per cycle, and the fuel the energy released when it is combusted with the available oxygen) and a given compression ratio (the maximum possible being determined by the knock rating of the fuel), the specific power output is effectively proportional to rpm. The rpm determines the rate at which air is passed through the engine and hence the rate at which fuel can be combusted with the oxygen in it. To realise the full potential of the combustion process, the volumetric efficiency, thermal efficiency, and mechanical efficiency must all be maintained as high as possible as the rpm increases.

Henri's Peugeot engine only produced 10.7hp/litre/1,000 rpm, compared to the Ferrari Tipo 049 engine's 14.7hp/litre/1,000rpm, partly because the compression ratio of the Peugeot was only 5.6:1, compared to the Ferrari's 12.0:1.

The Peugeot was limited by the fuels available in 1913, which had octane ratings of less than 60RON. It was not until the discovery of tetraethyl lead (TEL) by General Motors research scientists in 1921 and the push for a higher octane rating to accommodate the highly supercharged aero engines of World War II that the anti-detonation properties of the fuels permitted higher compression ratios when running on aviation petrol or the new pump fuels for road cars. By the 1960s, racing engines were able to run on pump petrol of around 95RON, and 3.0-litre Formula 1 engines generated around 13.5hp/litre/1,000rpm—not far short of today's engines. That engine designers have been able to increase this figure as RPM has doubled from the 9,000rpm of the engines in the 1960s to today's 18,000+rpm is testimony to their expertise and that of the regulation-restricted fuel chemists in keeping up the overall efficiency of the engine at greatly increased speeds and loads.

ABOVE: *The 3-litre normally aspirated 90-degree V-10 Tipo 049 engine produced more than 800hp at 17,500rpm during development in 2000.*

RIGHT: *Three views for the Tipo 049 Ferrari engine.*

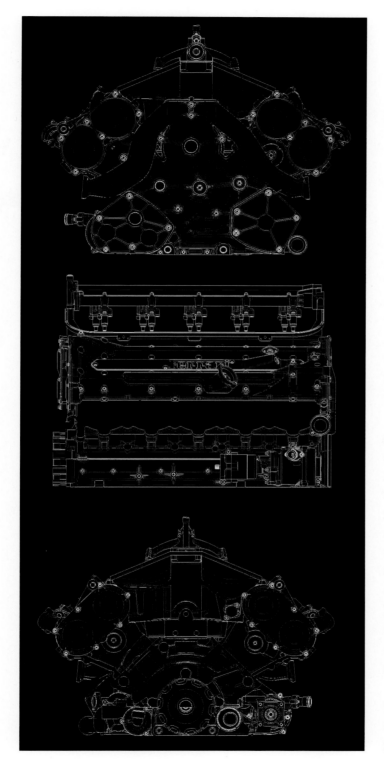

The FIA Formula 1 Technical Regulations covering engines puts restrictions on the swept volume, the cycle, and the specification of the fuel to be used by the engine. There are further limits on the number of cylinders and valves permitted and some of the materials that can be used. The former sets out to limit the available power and the latter to impose some limit to the costs of R&D and of building engines. Within these restrictions, the engine designer has only certain fundamentals he can change to improve performance. These are increasing rpm and increasing the volumetric, thermal, and mechanical efficiencies. As an added requirement, the chassis designer demands reduced size, weight, lower centre of gravity, and improved structural stiffness, especially at the joints where the engine is attached to the monocoque and gearbox. Virtually all the details of the engine arrangement and its components are determined by the need to fulfil these basic objectives for around 350kms.

The details of the Ferrari engine reveal how the problems generated by continuous development to meet the above objectives have been overcome and how solutions have been implemented. Increased rpm requires a larger bore-to-stroke ratio to reduce piston speed and acceleration; lighter reciprocating parts, such as pistons, connecting rods, and valves; stiffer rotating parts to push their natural frequencies in torsion above the increased excitation frequencies (e.g., crankshaft, gear train, and camshafts); damping systems to control torsional oscillations; a valve closing system that has no natural frequencies within the operating speed of the engine; and sufficiently robust components to withstand the vibration of a non-optimally balanced V-10 configuration.

To maintain volumetric efficiency, specialist software is used to minutely analyse the fluid flow and the resonance in the intake and exhaust passages and to model the unsteady flow in the combustion chamber. Although the desirability

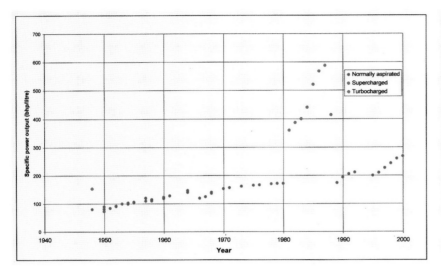

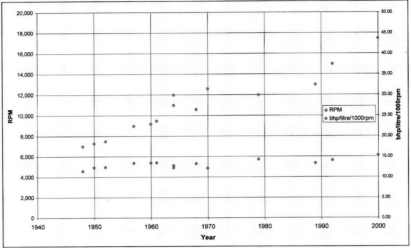

of varying the length of both the intakes and the exhaust pipes has been appreciated for many years, computer control of the engine now makes it feasible to vary the length of the intake trumpets. Applying the same technology to the exhausts is not permitted by the regulations, agreed to by the teams on the basis of cost.

Within the combustion chamber, it is impossible to separate volumetric and combustion requirements. Analysis of combustion and the test techniques to examine what occurs during the 150 times per second that each cylinder fires are among the most closely guarded technologies of every Formula 1 engine manufacturer. The 10-cylinder arrangement provides for the almost ideal 300cc swept volume per cylinder, but the large bore-to-stroke ratio that is driven by the rpm requirement results in a less-than-ideal combustion chamber shape—a large-diameter thin disc with valve pockets. Thermal efficiency also calls for management of heat rejection, balanced against material temperature limitations. The chassis designer wants smaller radiators, which means higher coolant temperatures, but this raises internal temperatures, particularly the piston, giving the engine designer more problems.

Control systems manage temperatures around the engine and optimise fuel delivery and ignition timing under all conditions. Control of fuel and ignition, along with trumpet length and drive-by-wire throttles, is used in such a way that under certain circumstances it is deliberately less than optimum, so the power output of the engine, as the rpm increases, is smoothed out for improved driveability.

Mechanical efficiency is the sum of internal engine losses plus the power consumed by the auxiliaries. Combinations of materials, finishes, and lubricant properties are used extensively to reduce friction between rubbing surfaces, and the size of bearings is minimised. Internal windage is reduced by compartmentalising the crankcase as five V-twins and using the scavenge pumps as oil/air pumps to reduce the pressure and air density in the crank chambers. Scavenging is so comprehensive that no excess oil is allowed anywhere in the engine to absorb precious power.

Auxiliary power demands have risen as the electrical loads have increased and a hydraulic pump has become standard fit. Driving the auxiliaries at higher rpm means they can be smaller and lighter, but this must always be balanced

ABOVE LEFT: *[Fig. 5-5] Specific power output for Ferrari GP engines from 1948 to 2000. Data is unavailable for some years. (Data Source:* Ferrari 1947–1997—The Official Book; *Ferrari)*

ABOVE RIGHT: *[Fig. 5-6] The rpm and specific power per 1,000rpm for Ferrari normally aspirated GP engines from 1948 to 2000. Data is unavailable for some years. (Data Source:* Ferrari 1947–1997—The Official Book; *Ferrari)*

against the inherent lower efficiency of high speeds.

Shorter stroke has enabled the crankshaft to be lowered and hence the centre of gravity. Clutch diameter reduction has matched this trend, until they vie with each other to not be the limiting factor. V-angle also affects C of G height, but many complications attend widening the V. The Ferrari's 90-degree angle brings all sorts of torsional vibration problems that then must be solved, compared to the V-10's ideal 72 degrees. Engines wider than 90 degrees fall into territory charted only by Renault in 2001 (rumoured to be using around 111 degrees), and it is not yet clear whether there is a net advantage in going much wider than 90 degrees.

Paolo Martinelli describes his development process: "We started with a V-angle close to the traditional 72 degrees, with even firing intervals, then in two steps to 90 degrees. The reason was to have some advantages in terms of vibration, but especially to reduce the height of the engine and its centre of gravity, while widening it to assist with the installation. The V-angle is not decided by just myself and Gilles, but Rory and Ross have a big say in it to ensure we arrive at the best package for the car." (See Figure 5-8.)

There are several feasible firing orders, each one a compromise between vibration levels, torsional excitation, and exhaust tuning. The firing order of the Tipo 049 engine, as illustrated and photographed, is as shown in Figure 5-10 on page 93. The intervals between cylinders firing are 90° - 54° - 90° - 54°, etc., at the crankshaft. It may not have been the same throughout the life of the engine, as Martinelli explains: "We look a lot at alternative firing orders, mainly to control vibration, to avoid peaks in the area of the revs where the engine spends 90 percent of its life and full

Baricentro

1) Motore 047/2 angolo V 80° altezza baricentro 204.5mm

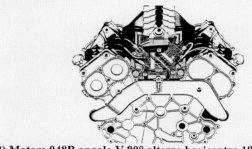

2) Motore 048B angolo V 80° altezza baricentro 197.5mm

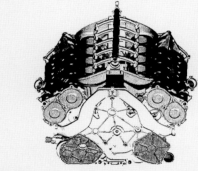

3) Motore 049 A angolo V 90° altezza baricentro 187mm

Diminuzione dell' altezza baricentro di <u>10.5mm</u> (confronto tra 048B e 049A)

throttle is used. There are of course fluid dynamic effects, both in the exhaust and the intakes, but vibration is the big issue."

As engines have shrunk in size and weight, they have progressively mismatched the back of the monocoque where they are attached. Spreading the loads from the small cross-section engine into the large fuel tank section requires careful detail design of both parts. Hot stiffness of the engine itself is determined mainly by the integrity of the joints between the main structural components, especially the sump/lower

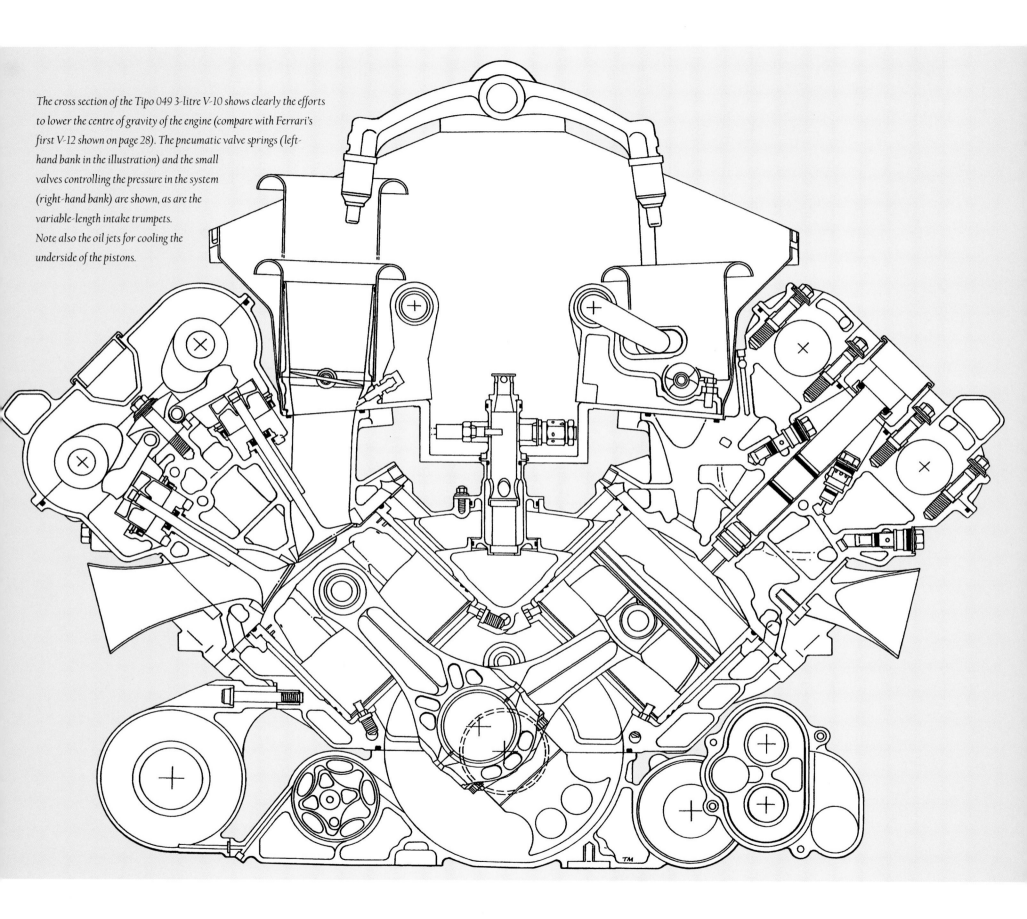

The cross section of the Tipo 049 3-litre V-10 shows clearly the efforts to lower the centre of gravity of the engine (compare with Ferrari's first V-12 shown on page 28). The pneumatic valve springs (left-hand bank in the illustration) and the small valves controlling the pressure in the system (right-hand bank) are shown, as are the variable-length intake trumpets. Note also the oil jets for cooling the underside of the pistons.

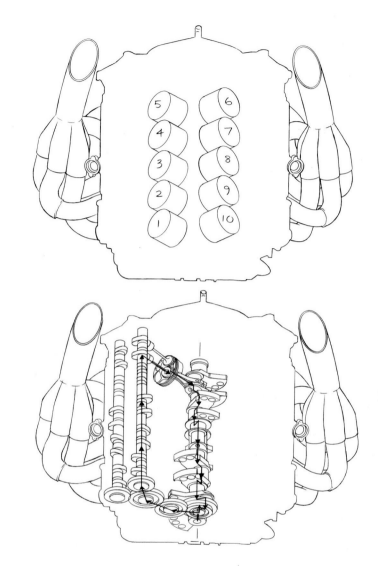

TOP: *[Fig. 5-10] Tipo 049 firing order is 1-10-5-6-2-9-3-8-4-7.*

RIGHT: *Torsional oscillations in the crankshaft, timing gears, and camshafts not only cause destructive peak stresses and fatigue, but also cause the phasing between pistons and their valves to fluctuate. The amplitude of the oscillations can significantly affect the valve timing, particularly of the rearmost cylinders. Torsional dampers are the secret of minimising these vibrations, but Ferrari did not permit divulgence of their whereabouts in the torsional path between crankshaft and cams.*

FAR RIGHT: *[Fig. 5-12] A power and torque curve for a Typo 049 engine from the Malaysian GP shows 806Cv at 17,500rpm and 35Kgm at 15,500rpm*

different circuits.

From these basic power and torque figures, it is possible to calculate some of the parameters that define engine performance:

Peak power   806CV at 17,500rpm
Peak torque   35Kgm at 15,500rpm
Maximum rpm   18,000rpm
b.m.e.p at peak power 13.4bar
b.m.e.p at peak torque 14.2bar
Mean piston speed at 18,000rpm 24.8m/s
Max. piston acceleration at 18,000rpm   8,890g

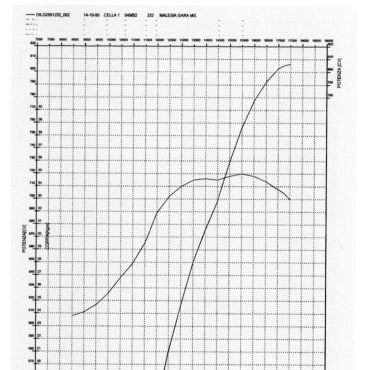

crankcase, crankcase/block, heads, and cam covers. At around 100kg, Formula 1 engines in 2000 weighed less than the 2.0-litre four-cylinder engines used in Formula 3. The latest engines in 2003 are reputed to weigh less than 90kg.

Figure 5-12 shows a typical power and torque curve for a Tipo 049 engine. Peak torque is 35Kgm at 15,500rpm, and peak power is 806CV or 817hp at 17,500rpm. (One CV, Ferrari's preferred unit of measure, equals 1.01387hp; CV stands for *cavallo vapore*, literally "vapor horse," from the days of steam power.) These figures are representative of the state of development late in 2000—at the Malaysian GP—and are just one of several engine tune characteristics available for

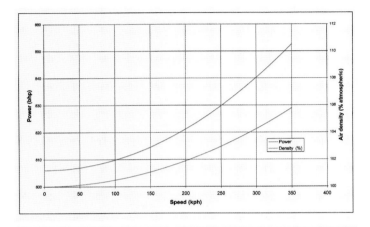

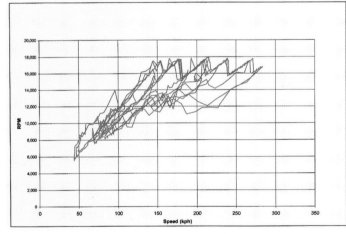

The power figures are for an engine tested under standard atmospheric conditions. All Formula 1 engine manufacturers have test beds where they can map and test engines under different intake air temperature and pressure conditions. Some generate the required intake conditions using heat exchangers and pressurising fans connected to a plenum chamber. Others also may have a wind tunnel with the working section above the engine on the dynamometer, into which extends the airbox from the car mounted normally onto the engine. Ferrari uses such an arrangement, simulating the airbox intake conditions at air speeds up to the maximum

speed of the car. This dynamometer is also used to validate CFD (computational fluid dynamics) and wind tunnel studies of the internal airbox shape to ensure that the air pressure and velocity conditions at each intake trumpet are correct—essential for individual cylinder fuel mapping.

A fair amount of wind tunnel time is spent on optimising the airbox: even the shape of the driver's helmet comes into the equation, and ram air energy recovery is close to 100 percent. At the maximum speed achieved on some circuits, around 350kph, this equates to 0.058bar, that is, a density increase of 5.8 percent. Under optimum conditions, this will raise the maximum potential power figure from 806 to 853CV (817 to 866hp; See Figure 5-13).

When the driver uses the engine to accelerate at full throttle through the gears, he employs a typical rpm band from 15,500rpm, peak torque, to 18,000rpm, at which point the power has fallen off to around the same value as at 16,000rpm—see Figure 5-14, which plots RPM against car speed for Michael Schumacher's best qualifying lap at Monaco. This illustrates the gear ratios used and also that there is wheel spin in all gears up to fourth gear. Accelerating out of corners, on part throttle, he allows the rpm to fall as low as 8,000 in second and third gears and as low as 6,000 in first gear. The wheel spin peaks indicate that there is an excess of power over traction and that allowing the rpm to fall way down the torque curve is not detrimental to acceleration and is undoubtedly beneficial for driveability.

In fourth gear and above, 12,000rpm is generally the minimum the engine is allowed to fall to, which is the engine speed when the torque reaches 90 percent of its peak. The torque and power curves from 12,000 to 17,500rpm display only one dip, at 14,500rpm. Such a smooth torque curve on a high-revving racing engine is the result of a great deal of tuning optimisation, in particular in the development of the control laws for the moveable intake trumpets.

TOP LEFT: *[Fig. 5-13] Ram air, collected by the airbox, increases air density proportional to the speed of the car squared. The effect on maximum power of 100 percent ram pressure recovery is shown in the graph.*

BOTTOM LEFT : *[Fig. 5-14] In qualifying for Monaco, Schumacher uses 18,000rpm in the gears, dropping to 15,500 to 16,000rpm, just on peak torque, on up changes. In the corners, he allows the rpm to drop as low as 8,000 and even 6,000 in first gear.*

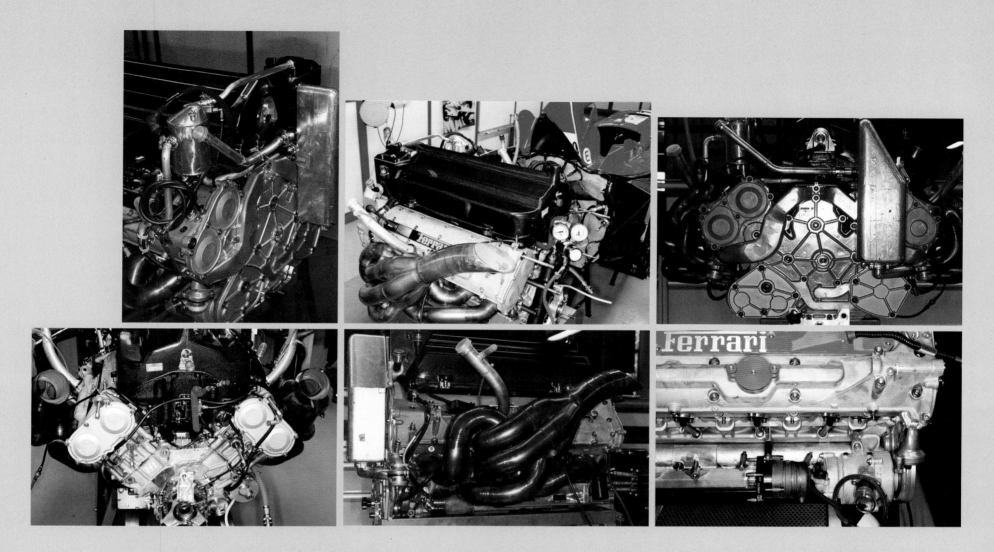

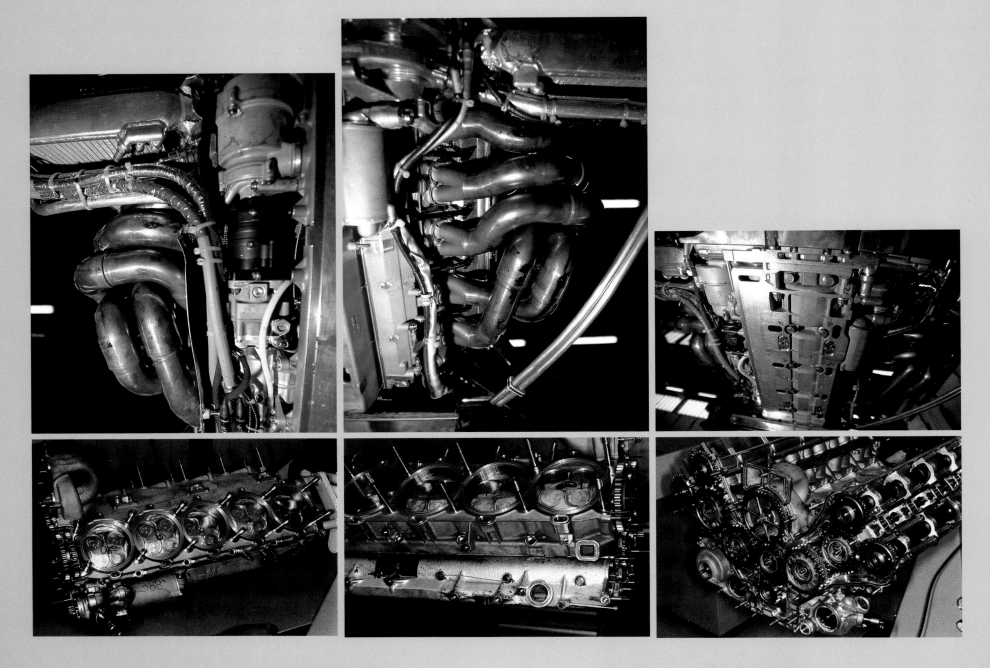

TOP ROW (LEFT TO RIGHT): ■ *The auxiliaries on the right side of the engine are the air/oil de-aerator, the alternator, and the hydraulic pump, all driven at 71.5 percent of engine speed. Behind the hydraulic pump is the pressurised hydraulic reservoir.*

■ *The auxiliaries on the left side of the engine consist of a scavenge pump to empty the timing gear case, the oil pump, its filter, and, behind this assembly, the auxiliary oil reservoir.*

■ *The underside of the engine displays the main bearing bolts, the bottom engine-mounting studs, and fasteners for the attachment of the undertray.*

BOTTOM ROW (LEFT TO RIGHT): ■ *The block/crankcase is a compact aluminium investment casting. Wet liners are fitted, in which the Mahle pistons run. The canister behind the oil pressure pump is the oil filter.*

■ *Beneath the block, on the right-hand side of the engine, lies a cylinder running the length of the block, into which are inserted eleven Eaton-type scavenge oil pumps. A common shaft drives them via the timing gears.*

■ *The camshafts are driven by a gear train at the front of the engine, which also drives the auxiliaries down the sides of the engine, and the water pump, which is mounted high in the V.*

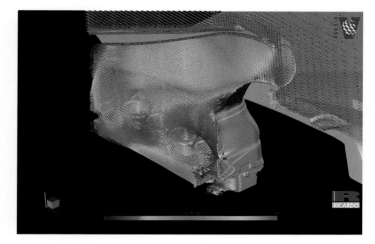

FAR RIGHT: *This illustration shows the velocity distribution inside the airbox. The small variation in velocity and hence pressure around the intake trumpets can be seen. The highest velocities are shown in red and the lowest in blue—the darkest blue representing static high-pressure air.*

RIGHT: *[Fig. 5-27] The intake trumpet length is varied with rpm to optimise the resonant tuning. The programmed schedule depends on the desired shaping of the torque curve and will typically cycle three or four times over the working rpm range, as shown here.*

BELOW RIGHT: *[Fig. 5-28] The throttles on the two banks of cylinders are operated independently to phase in the power progressively as the driver opens the throttles. Up to 30 percent difference between the two banks may be programmed at low throttle openings. The leading and lagging throttles are swapped over, side to side, each time the throttle is fully closed, in order to avoid one bank having to work harder than the other all the time.*

Typical characteristics of the trumpet control are illustrated in Figure 5-27, which shows how the length is cycled a number of times over the working rpm range to optimise the resonance in the intake ducts. Optimisation may not mean achieving maximum power at every rpm, for compromises are made to achieve a smooth torque curve. While accelerating in the lower gears, rpm changes at more than 25,000rpm/second and at a higher rate during gear changes. The trumpet actuation system must track these rpm change rates and requires powerful hydraulic actuators to do so.

Ferrari developed a number of additional techniques for smoothing the torque curve and managing the power as the

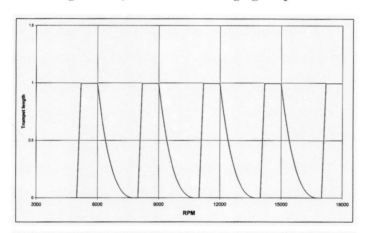

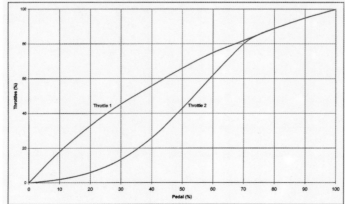

throttles are opened. The drive-by-wire throttles allow non-linear characteristics between the accelerator pedal position and the throttle butterflies. However, even this is not enough to control the sudden increase in torque as the throttles are opened. The throttles for the left and right banks are actuated independently by hydraulic actuators and open the butterflies at different rates (Figure 5-28). In this way, the engine is run as two five-cylinder engines, with a 20 to 30 percent difference in the magnitude of the throttle openings until around 80 percent of full throttle. To avoid wearing out one side of the engine before the other, every time the throttles are shut the banks swap over which one will lead with its throttle opening. Phasing of fuel injection and alterations to the ignition timing were also used to shape the torque curve at part throttle.

Ferrari's Tipo 049 engine is number six in a steadily evolving series of V-10 engines. There have been three more since, as of 2003, and several intermediate -A, -B, and -C versions of each. The 049 is a point on a rising curve—at some stage in 2000 during its development, the engineers in the test cells at Maranello passed another threshold when they watched a normally aspirated Ferrari engine exceed 800CV and 18,000 rpm for the first time. Developments in Formula 1 are relentless—

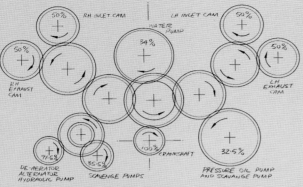

■ *The timing gears drive the four overhead camshafts, the auxiliaries grouped low alongside the engine, and the high-mounted water pump. Intermediate gears ensure that each auxiliary is driven at the most efficient speed.*

TOP ROW (LEFT TO RIGHT): ■ *The timing gears. The large-diameter gear in the centre drives the high-mounted water pump. Additional gears (not fitted here) along the bottom of the front of the engine drive the oil pump on the left side of the engine (shown on the right in this photograph); the scavenge pumps are on the right side, next to the crankcase; and the de-aerator, alternator, and hydraulic pump are on the same side, farther outboard.*

■ *Camshafts operate the four valves per cylinder via finger followers, which absorb the side load on the valve stem at the lowest weight. The valves are splayed in side elevation, and the followers also accommodate the misalignment with the cams. Dummy camshaft bearing caps replace those machined integral with the cam covers.*

■ *This combustion chamber detail shows the way in which the maximum valve area has been fitted into the bore dimension.*

BOTTOM ROW (LEFT TO RIGHT): ■ *Looking down the linered cylinder bore, one can see the tangential slot through which the rotating crankshaft slings oil to be picked up by the twin scavenge pumps assigned to each "V-twin" crankcase.*

■ *The investment-cast front timing cover incorporates the water passages from the radiator to the water pump.*

■ *The cam cover forms a major load path between the monocoque, engine, and transmission. The cast-in boss at the front forms the top mounting between monocoque and engine, and the long stud at the rear picks up the CFRP bell housing and also the upper rear suspension member.*

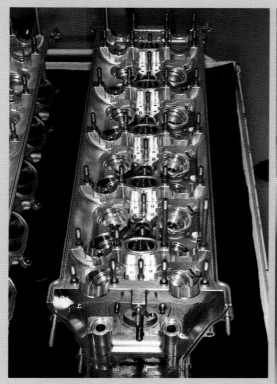

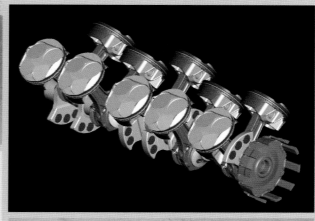
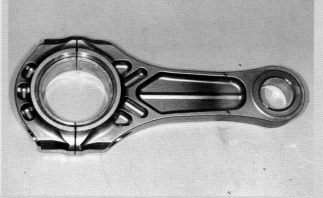

CLOCKWISE (LEFT TO RIGHT): ▪ *The sand-cast aluminium cylinder head has four valves per cylinder. Each of the valves in a pair is splayed 3 degrees from the cylinder axis to make room for the camshaft bearing between them and to provide for slightly greater valve area.*

▪ *The crankshaft is machined from a steel billet and has its crank pins set at 72 degrees. Counter-balance webs are drilled and filled with tungsten inserts to increase their mass.*

▪ *It is possible to get some appreciation of the compactness of Ferrari's 90 degree V-10, with its bore-to-stroke ratio of 2.32:1, from this CAD image.*

▪ *This forged titanium connecting rod has benefited from FEA to enable every unnecessary part to be machined away. Note the ridged hole feeding oil from the big end to the little end.*

▪ *The four valve pockets form a significant part of the combustion chamber when the forged aluminium piston is at top dead centre. The mass of the piston is minimised to reduce inertia loads at high RPM, and the skirt sealing land, with single compression and oil control rings, is as narrow as possible to reduce friction. Cooling is enhanced by squirting oil from jets onto the underside.*

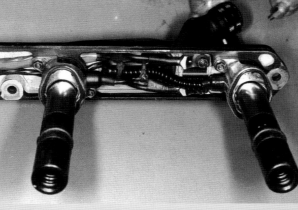

▪ Miscellaneous engine parts, including timing gears and Eaton scavenge oil pumps.

▪ The Magneti Marelli coil-on-plug igniters insert deep into the cylinder heads to connect with the spark plugs.

▪ The oil de-aerator centrifugally separates the large volume of air from the oil drawn from the five individual V-twin crankcases. The capacity of the scavenge pumps is such that the crankshaft runs in a partial vacuum to reduce windage losses.

▪ The intake and exhaust valves are both titanium. The exhaust valve is sprayed with ceramic.

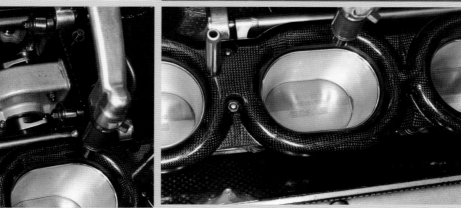

TOP ROW (LEFT TO RIGHT): ▪ The tiny (62mm diam. x 98.5mm long) Magneti Marelli alternator delivers 41.2 amps at 9,000rpm and can be driven at more than 12,5000rpm.

▪ CAD and CAM make it possible to create this assembly of oil pressure pump and scavenge pump, integrated with their manifolds.

BOTTOM ROW (LEFT TO RIGHT): ▪ The gearbox nestling in the V turns the inputs from three actuators, mounted in the bell housing, into the drives for the independent throttles of each bank and the variable-length intake trumpets.

▪ The CFRP intake trumpets slide on pillars around the butterfly throttle body to vary the tuned length of the intakes.

▪ The magnificent fuel rail and injectors.

that is until the FIA trims them back to keep performance within safe and reasonable bounds. One can only speculate how high the next peak will be.

FERRARI'S TECHNICAL PARTNER FOR THE ENGINE: MAHLE.
Mahle was founded in 1920, as an innovative manufacturer of lightweight alloy pistons. Today the group supplies pistons, liners, filters, and valve train systems to the automotive industry worldwide, with annual sales exceeding €2.8 billion, and more than 28,000 employees.

Since the early 1930s, racing engine designers have sought out Mahle to develop and supply pistons and liners for their highly stressed creations. Mahle now supplies these components to virtually all the leading engine manufacturers in Formula 1, World Rallying, CART, IRL, and NASCAR, as well as many other series around the world.

Ferrari Tipo 049 Engine Specifications

Configuration	90-degree V-10
Capacity	2,997cc
Bore	96.0mm
Stroke	41.4mm
Bore-to-stroke ratio	2.32 to 1
Compression ratio	12.0 to 1
Length	615mm to rear face of flywheel
Width	597.6mm
Height	365.5mm
Weight	less than 106kg ("C" spec). Incl.: clutch; excl.: exhaust, ECU
C of G height	187mm ("A" spec)
Firing order	1-10-5-6-2-9-3-8-4-7 (RH front cyl.: 1; LH rear cyl.: 6; see Figure 5-10 on page 93)
Valve actuation	Twin overhead camshafts per bank; finger followers; pneumatic return springs—200 bar, 0.7-litre reservoir
Valve included angle	25.0 degrees in transverse section; 6.0 degrees in longitudinal section
Camshaft drive	Gears at front of engine
Engine management system	Magneti Marelli, step 9

Fuel	Pump petrol to FIA specification; Shell
Fuel system	Magneti Marelli digital electronic injection, one injector/cyl.; 10 bar; gear pump in tank, driven from front of engine
Ignition system	Magneti Marelli digital electronic; coil-on-plug
Cooling system	Water; 3.5bar normal; 3.75bar max.; centrifugal pump at 34 percent engine speed
Oil pressure system	1-2bar; gear pump at 32.5 percent engine speed; Shell oil
Oil scavenge system	Eleven Eaton scavenge pumps at 35.5 percent engine speed; one Eaton scavenge pump at 32.5 percent engine speed; oil/air separator at 71.5 percent engine speed
Throttle actuation system	Electrohydraulic actuated butterflies; separate control of each bank
Variable-length intake system	Electrohydraulic; CFRP trumpets
Block	Investment-cast aluminium alloy, 7 percent silicon
Liners	Wet; aluminium/Nickasil coated
Heads	Sand-cast aluminium
Structural covers	Investment-cast aluminium
Nonstructural covers	CFRP
Crankshaft	Vacuum-cast, extruded steel; six main bearings; tungsten balance weights
Camshafts	Vacuum-cast, extruded steel
Valves	Intake: 40.4mm diam., titanium
	Exhaust: 33.0mm diam., titanium, ceramic coated
Valve lift	Intake: 15.5mm
	Exhaust: 14.1mm
Pistons	Forged aluminium; Mahle
Connecting rods	Forged titanium
Torsional dampers	Not disclosed
Exhaust pipes	Inconel; five-into-one

© Tony Mathews '02

6

Transmission

*T*he transmission of the F1-2000 follows contemporary
Formula 1 practice in its layout, but is unique in its method of
construction. Ferrari has used this longitudinal layout and CFRP
(carbon-fibre-reinforced plastic)/titanium construction design since
1998, but its history dates back to 1994, when John Barnard, then Technical Director of Ferrari,
determined to move from magnesium as the material of choice for gear cases, because of its
hot stiffness and precise casting limitations.

LEFT: *The complete transmission cutaway illustration.*

ABOVE: *A detail of the final drive and the epicyclic gears of the differential.*

Barnard designed a transverse gearbox for the 412 T1, the case of which was made up as a fabricated steel box, with the sides machined out of 25mm plate, CNC-milled down to 1.2mm wall thickness and ribs. The gear case weighed only a little less than the magnesium one it replaced, which was a disappointment, and so in mid-season the switch was made to titanium instead of steel, yielding an immediate 40 percent weight reduction (Figure 6-3 on page 106).

For 1995, the fabricated titanium gear case was bolted to a CFRP bell housing/oil tank, onto which the suspension units were mounted and into which the majority of the suspension loads were fed. The '94 and '95 gearboxes were a three-bearing arrangement, but in 1996 a two-bearing design was used. A CFRP rear impact crash structure was also fitted in 1996, albeit one year ahead of the FIA requirement. The same basic arrangement—CFPR bell housing/titanium fabricated gear case and rear case/CFRP impact structure—has been in use at Ferrari ever since, but in a longitudinal layout since 1998.

Ross Brawn considers that the gearbox arrangement his team inherited did not exploit all the potential of the construction method. The transmission consisted of a titanium gearbox with a CFRP bell housing/oil tank and was quite heavy, not truly justifying the effort involved in manufacturing

final drive. The speed reduction from the engine (maximum 18,000rpm) to the driven rear wheels (maximum 2,800rpm) requires a 0.156 speed reduction and is accomplished in three stages. The first stage is the gear cluster, the output shaft of which drives an intermediate shaft via spiral-bevel gears (0.61 speed reduction). The third stage is the straight-cut final drive gear pair (0.306 reduction is shown in Figure 6-6 on page 108), giving an overall 0.186 reduction for the final two stages. Three alternative gear pairs (14/50, 14/52, 15/49) for the final stage are available.

Changing the installed ratios is carried out through the front bearing housing cover plate, and the gearbox must be separated from the engine to do so. While this inevitably takes longer than on a longitudinal gearbox with the gears behind the final drive or on a transverse gearbox, neither of which require removal of the gearbox, it is not a major inconvenience, as changing ratios is much less common than it used to be. Seven speeds, semi-automatic gear selection, extensive track testing, and accurate simulations all add up to the correct ratios normally being fitted at the factory for a GP event and requiring no further changes during the weekend (Figure 6-5).

CONSTRUCTION.

The gearbox itself is constructed by welding twenty-four machined titanium sections together (Figure 6-10 on page 111). The sections are CNC-machined on all surfaces, giving precise control over all dimensions. The ability to machine details, often inaccessible inside a cast casing, is an additional benefit of this construction. The casing carries the suspension loads generated by the rear legs of each wishbone and the toe-control link and the loads generated by the dampers. The inboard mountings of the rear leg of the lower wishbones are integrated into the bearing housings of the second-stage speed-reduction shaft on both sides. A through bolt, inside

it that way. A programme of weight reduction was set up that resulted in the 2000 car's transmission having a CFRP basic structure into which all the main suspension loads are fed, with the titanium gear case mounted beneath it and forming the rear of the structure where it rises up to the final drive unit.

GEAR LAYOUT.

The F1-2000 transmission is a seven-speed-plus-reverse longitudinal gearbox, with the gears mounted ahead of the

TOP LEFT: *[Fig. 6-3] The first fabricated titanium gearbox from the 1994 412T1. Originally fabricated in steel, it offered no weight saving and so the material was changed to titanium.*

LEFT: *[Fig. 6-4] This semiautomatic gear-change system was developed in 1979–80 for the 312T4. It never raced, but it predated the system on the 1989 Tipo 640 by ten years.*

RIGHT: *[Fig. 6-5] The longitudinal section drawing of the gearbox shows the pull-action clutch, mounted to the engine, and compact seven-speed gear cluster. The dog rings, with their internal dogs, save around 6 mm per gear in the length of the cluster, compared to face dogs. The final drive is in two stages, with an intermediate shaft driven by a bevel gear from the gear cluster output shaft. This arrangement allows for the difference in height between the input from the low crankshaft and the final drive at around wheel centre height.*

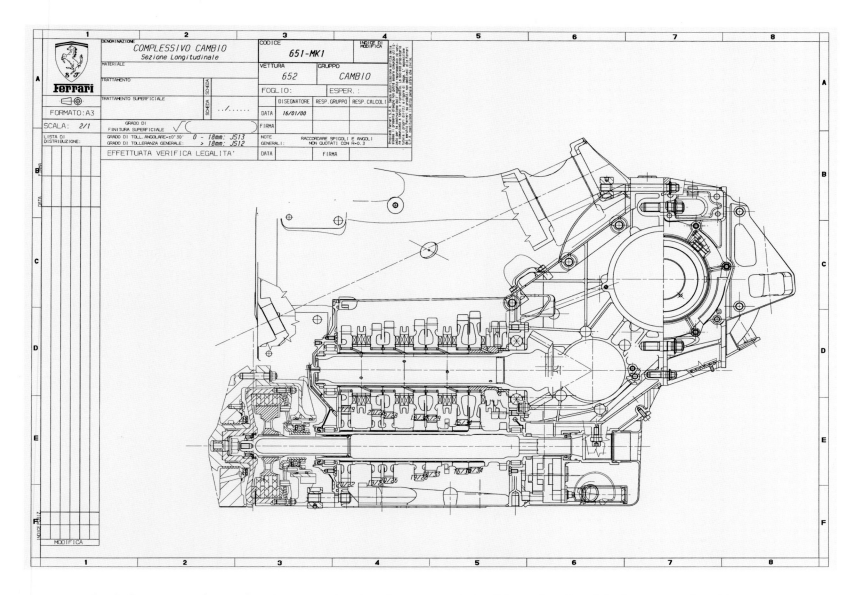

the shaft, connects the two housings, ensuring that the combined suspension loads and the thrust load of the bevel gear are borne by both sides of the casing at all times.

The rear CFRP wing/rear impact structure is bolted to the removable final drive cover.

The gear case is connected to the engine via a CFRP moulding, which incorporates the forward wishbone mountings and the suspension rocker pivots, such that their loads and the reactive loads on the torsion bar springs are fed into it. The forward wishbone mountings are integrated into the mounting points between the CFRP bell housing and the engine, ensuring a direct load path into the engine. The rear

anti-roll bar, when fitted, is also mounted to this structure.

There are no fluid tanks in the bell housing. Some of the space above the clutch and gears is utilised to mount the actuators that control the engine throttles and trumpets. As the main hydraulic control manifold also is mounted on the gearbox, this means that the minimum number of contamination-critical hydraulic lines have to be broken when the gearbox is detached from the engine during changes to the engine or gearbox.

Also passing through this space are cooling ducts, fed with air from above the filter in the airbox, for damper and clutch cooling.

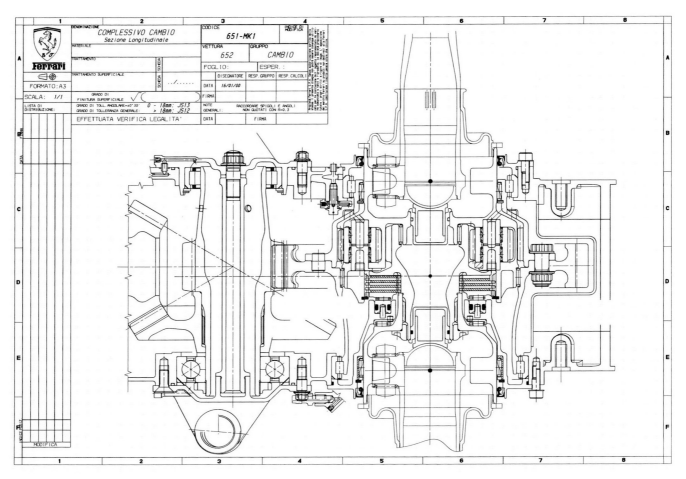

FORMATO: A3

SCALA: 1/1

EFFETTUATA VERIFICA LEGALITA'

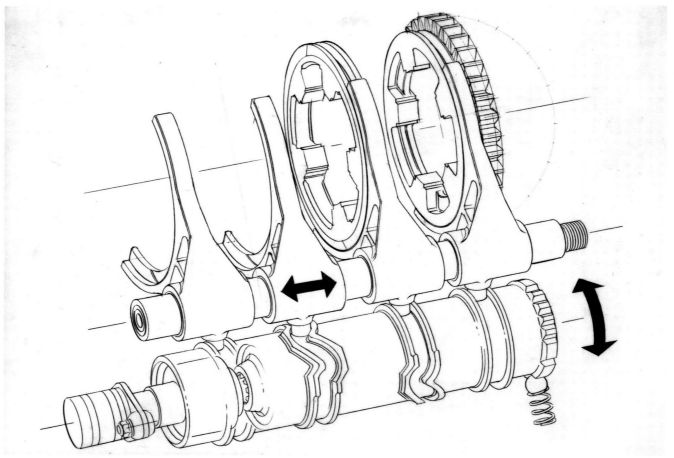

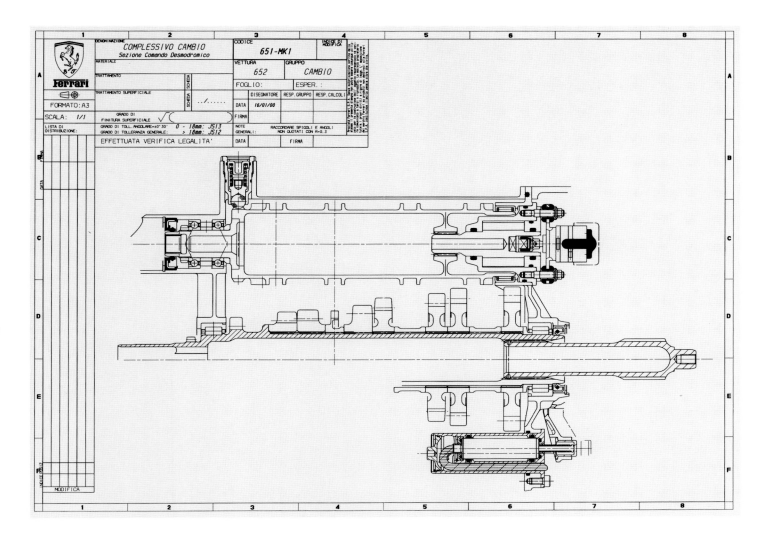

Much of the detail design of the combined titanium casing and CFRP bell housing is to ensure a stiff load path between the rear suspension and the main structure. The joint between the two parts and the way in which the suspension loads are fed into each of them have obviously been conceived with this objective in mind. The fact that Ferrari has not made the step to an all-CFRP gearbox underlines the importance that the designers place on the need to provide the precise location for the gear shaft bearings under high gear parting loads and when subjected to high gearbox temperatures. They are apparently not convinced that overcoming the sealing and expansion coefficient problems (negative in the case of CFRP), which those who have developed CFRP gearboxes have had to solve, are worth the risks involved for a small weight benefit.

GEAR SELECTION.

Gear selection is carried out by the rotation of a barrel, which sequentially moves the selector forks to engage the seven gears and reverse (Figure 6-7). Pegs on the forks engage in grooves in the circumference of the barrel; the four grooves have zigzag sections, indexed relative to each other, which move the appropriate selector forward or backward to engage the gear via a dog ring. The first gear selector also engages reverse, by meshing gear teeth on the dog ring with an idler gear.

The dog rings have internal dogs, which engage with face dogs on the gears. This arrangement was first used in the 1994 gearbox, saving around 6mm per dog ring and hence, 18 mm overall on the width of the six-speed transverse arrangement.

Barrel rotation on semi-automatic and automatic gear-boxes can be achieved by three basic means: a linear actuator driving a ratchet, as per the foot-change on a motorcycle; a linear actuator driving the rack of a rack and pinion; or a rotary actuator, as used by Ferrari (Figure 6-8 on page 109). The vane-type actuator is fitted inside the barrel, with the rotary sensor driven by a coupling, mounted outside. It provides the smallest, lightest, and most precise system. A ratchet actuator can be driven open loop (as with a foot-change sequential motorcycle gearbox, the ratchet mechanism allows control in one direction only), but complete control of the selection sequence timing and the need to perform "retries" if the change is balked requires closed-loop control, which is best achieved with either the second or third option.

A notched ring on the rear end of the barrel provides detents for the neutral and in-gear positions. A special tool can be inserted externally into the rear end of the barrel to provide a means of manual gear selection when the car is stationary.

FINAL DRIVE AND DIFFERENTIAL.

The design of the final drive is dictated by the desire to make it as narrow as possible, as it locally dictates the width of the underbody diffuser. The tripod constant-velocity joints are placed as near the centre line of the car as is possible, and the electro-hydraulically controlled limited-slip differential is situated between them. The differential is an epicyclic-gear type, using five pairs of sun gears running on needle bearings. A three- or four-plate clutch, the clamping load on which is applied by an annular hydraulic cylinder, controls friction across the differential (Figure 6-6 on page 108).

LUBRICATION AND COOLING.

Lubrication and cooling are provided by a wet sump and single-gear pump, picking up oil from the rear of the gearbox, and supplying it to the gears and bearings via a single row of

the engine oil radiator. Oil is pumped directly to the main shaft bearings and via jets to the bevel and final drive gears. It is also fed into the secondary gear shaft, whence, under centrifugal force it is fed to the needle roller bearings on which the gears run. Oil leaves these bearings as a mist to lubricate the gears and other bearings. Additionally, oil is fed to the selector-mounting shaft, the internal volume of which is minimised by an internal spindle, and lubricates, via drillings, the selectors' linear bearings and the rubbing surfaces between the selectors and the dog rings.

Oil also is fed to the differential gears by jets, and the resulting mist lubricates the final drive and differential bearings.

CLUTCH.

A 4.5-inch triple-plate diaphragm-spring carbon-carbon clutch is used to transmit power from the engine to the gearbox. Its actuation is by an annular hydraulic cylinder pulling on the inside of the diaphragm spring. By turning the cylinder round to pull, as opposed to the more conventional push operation, the whole clutch actuation system is mounted to the engine and does not rely on the precise location of the gearbox. A sensor measures the position of the

LEFT: *The right side of the gearbox is almost hidden by the hydraulic manifold and sensor connector box. Extensive heat shielding is used to protect hydraulics, electrics, and the damper from exhaust heat.*

RIGHT: *[Fig. 6-10] The titanium gear case is fabricated by welding twenty-four CNC-machined parts together in an inert gas atmosphere.*

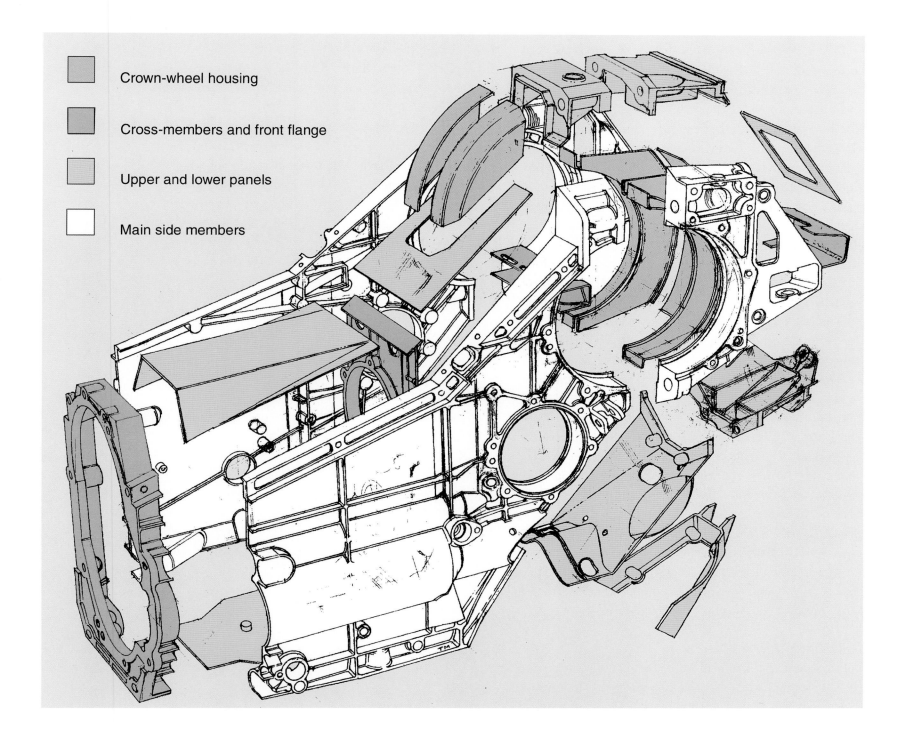

Crown-wheel housing

Cross-members and front flange

Upper and lower panels

Main side members

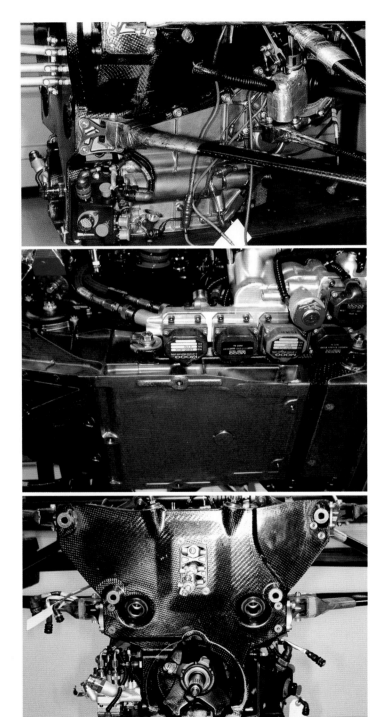

actuator piston, because the take-up point of the clutch, which varies as the clutch wears, is an essential measurement for the control software.

The diameter of the clutch is larger than the smallest clutches used in Formula 1 (4-inch diameter), where great efforts are made to minimise the diameter, as it determines how low the crankshaft centreline can be in the car, with the associated benefit of a lower C of G height. The critical duty cycle for the clutch is at the start, which provides one of the few opportunities for overtaking, and Ferrari's choice of a larger clutch points to the importance placed on the clutch's capacity and consistent characteristics. Semi-automatic gear changing does not disengage the clutch during up-shifts, and may do so only momentarily during downshifts in order to smooth the torque to the rear wheels during hard braking, when the engine may be forced to accelerate suddenly as the lower gear engages.

ENGINE STARTING.
Inserting the off-car starter shaft to engage in the rear of the input shaft enables the engine to be started.

In 2002, Ferrari changed to investment-cast titanium for its gear cases, and the beautiful, almost jewel-like fabricated titanium gearboxes they had used for eight years are consigned to museums, where the intricacies of their construction and the skill in welding them can be admired by all.

TOP LEFT: The left side of the gearbox and rear suspension. The through-rod damper is shrouded for cooling.

MIDDLE LEFT: The view from under the gearbox shows the hydraulic manifold and Moog servo-valves.

BOTTOM LEFT: The front face of the CFRP gearbox bell housing shows the ends of the suspension torsion bars, the ride-height adjusters, and the three actuators for the throttles and trumpets, which connect to the engine when attached.

TOP ROW (LEFT TO RIGHT): ■ *The 4.5-inch pull-operated clutch is actuated by a concentric hydraulic cylinder in the "spider" casting surrounding it. The extension arm operates a position sensor to allow the take-up point of the clutch to be monitored precisely.*

■ *This titanium end cover must be removed to enable the changing of gear ratios.*

■ *The fabricated titanium main case.*

■ *The fabricated titanium final drive cover and bearing caps. The rear impact structure and wing mounting are bolted to this cover.*

BOTTOM ROW (LEFT TO RIGHT): ■ *The main case with CFRP bell housing attached. The bell housing accepts all the suspension vertical loads.*

■ *A view from the underneath of the main case, from the rear.*

■ *An inside view of the main case. This detail would be impossible to machine if the case was not fabricated from machined pieces.*

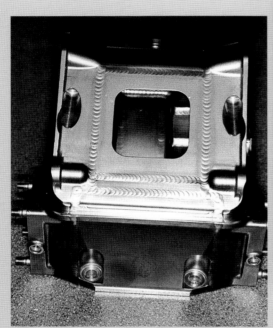

LEFT: ▪ *Exquisite welding of titanium is one of the keys to the mode of construction of the gear case.*

RIGHT: ▪ *The titanium gear case and CFRP bell housing.*

TOP ROW (LEFT TO RIGHT): ■ *The CFRP bell housing joins the gearbox to the engine and carries the majority of the rear suspension loads.*

■ *The CFRP bell housing—engine interface. The bosses on the top mount the adjusters for the torsion bar springs to permit rear ride-height changes to be made easily. The square aperture is where the three actuators for the engine throttles and trumpets pass through to connect to the engine.*

■ *The CFRP bell housing from the rear, showing the internal ducting for clutch and damper cooling. The moulding is a complex structure, carrying all the rear suspension loads into the car.*

BOTTOM ROW (LEFT TO RIGHT): ■ *Selector dog ring, showing the internal dogs, engaged with the face dogs on the gear. The ends of the internal dogs engage in recesses in the dog ring sleeve.*

■ *The selector fork and its peg, which engages in the zig-zag track on the selector barrel.*

115

TOP ROW (LEFT TO RIGHT) ▪ *The sleeves on which the dog rings slide are splined to the upper output shaft of the gearbox.*

▪ *The final drive gear pair.*

▪ *The gearbox input shaft.*

BOTTOM ROW (LEFT TO RIGHT) ▪ *The bevel gear pair and output shaft. One dog ring sleeve is fitted.*

▪ *The oil pump drive gears. The pump is driven from the input shaft.*

▪ *A differential set of epicyclic gears.*

TOP ROW (LEFT TO RIGHT): ■ *The electro-hydraulically actuated, adjustable epicyclic differential.*

■ *Selector barrel showing the zig-zag tracks, into which the pegs on the selector forks engage. The vane-type rotary actuator fits inside the barrel to drive it.*

■ *The gear-type oil pump and idler gear. The pump must be able to pass the inevitable steel chips that a dog engagement system generates. The end faces of the gears show witness of this.*

BOTTOM ROW (LEFT TO RIGHT): ■ *These are the main gearbox internals, except bearings.*

■ *The differential and tripod joint outer.*

■ *The final drive.*

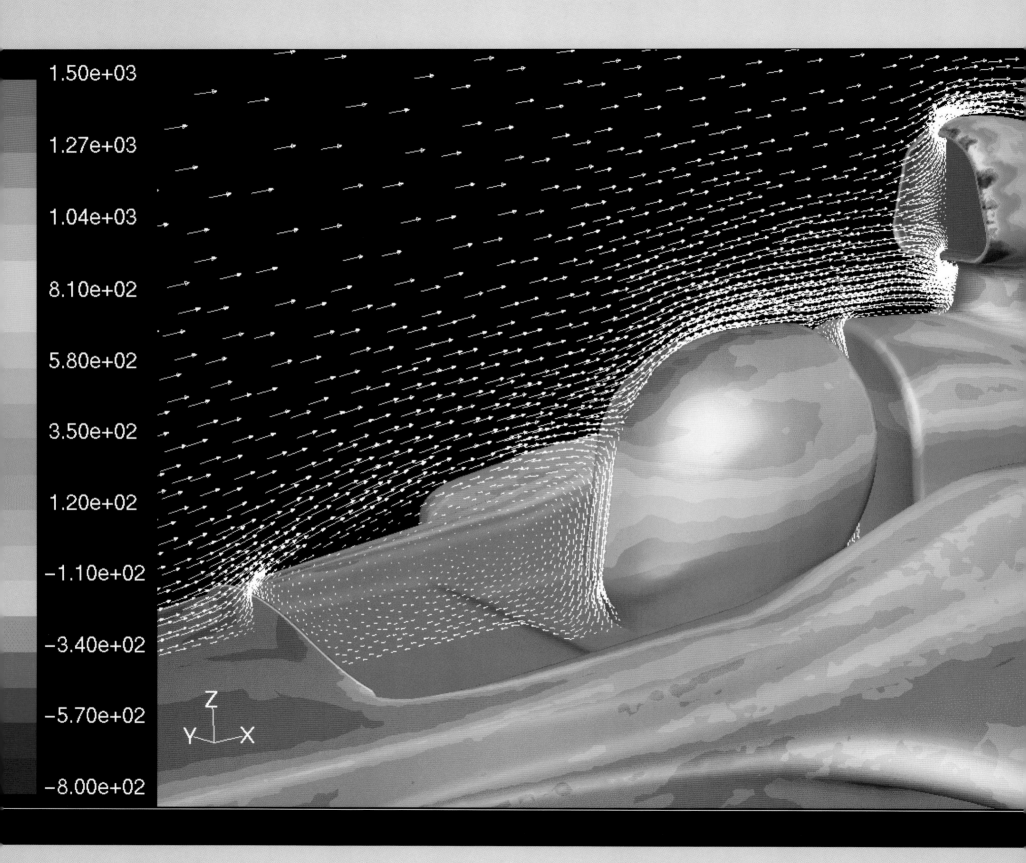

7

Aerodynamics

Ever since Ferrari appeared at the Belgian GP at Spa in 1968, fitted with a strut-mounted inverted wing above the engine, the pursuit of downforce on Formula 1 cars has expanded almost exponentially to the point where it consumes more R&D effort than any other part of the car, except perhaps the engine. The maximum downforce available, along with the efficiency (lift/drag ratio) and the dynamic aerodynamic characteristics, joins the engine and the tyres in determining the overall performance of the car.*

LEFT: *CFD analysis of the critical flow around the driver's head and into the engine intake shows velocity vectors (length of arrows is proportional to wind speed).*

RIGHT: *This detail of the barge board from Tony Matthews's cutaway drawing of the car illustrates the complexity of modern Formula 1 car aerodynamics.*

The blind pursuit of downforce without due consideration of the characteristics and interactions between the wings body, and other parts of the car affecting its aerodynamics has been the downfall of many Formula 1 designs, especially since the development of ground effect in the late 1970s. Most designers now understand the relationships and trade-offs between downforce and drag for each circuit; how to adjust them; how to achieve stability derived by using the pitch, heave, roll, and yaw characteristics of the car as it moves relative to the ground; how to dissipate the reject heat from engine, gearbox, and brakes; and how to exploit the engine power benefits from ram air and, to a certain extent, the influence of the wake of a car in front. Today the aerodynamics departments of Formula 1 teams have expensive and sophisticated tools available to enable calculation (CFD), simulation (wind tunnel), and full-size testing (track) to be brought to bear on the design of the all-important wings, undertray, side pods, and body. Literally thousands of tiny variations in the surfaces are evaluated and tested in the search for a few percent of L/D each year and improved dynamic characteristics.

So successful have been these aerodynamic R&D programmes and so great the effect on the cars' performance that the FIA has been forced to progressively regulate those parts

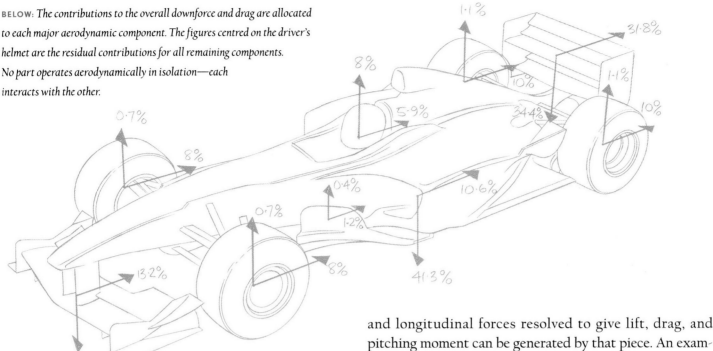

BELOW: *The contributions to the overall downforce and drag are allocated to each major aerodynamic component. The figures centred on the driver's helmet are the residual contributions for all remaining components. No part operates aerodynamically in isolation—each interacts with the other.*

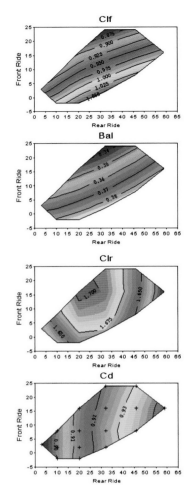

of the car that have the most influence. The effect has been to reduce the available gains per year, in spite of the ever-increasing resources brought to bear on the subject, and to converge the aerodynamic performance of the different cars. Designers and aerodynamicists are beginning to take a broader overall look at the layout of the cars to see whether there are net gains to be had from changes to it. Proper understanding of the tyres, weight distribution, suspension dynamics, engine intake, exhaust, and cooling flows and of their contributions to vehicle dynamics is now possible through simulation. Applying this understanding to alter the layout of the car to the benefit of the aerodynamics, without detracting from the performance of any other characteristic, is true systems engineering and is likely to provide significant performance gains in spite of continuing regulation.

With validated CFD software becoming a major tool in aerodynamic design, it is possible to separate the contribution to downforce and drag of the most significant individual parts of the car. Surface pressure calculations can be integrated over a specified surface, and the vertical

and longitudinal forces resolved to give lift, drag, and pitching moment can be generated by that piece. An examination of the contributions of the wings, underfloor, and wheels of the Ferrari F1-2000 provide a guide to where the development effort is focused and to the development objectives (Table 7-1).

The undertray, with its rear diffuser working in ground effect, is the most efficient component, producing more than 40 percent of the downforce for just 10 percent of the drag.

TABLE 7-1: CL AND CD CONTRIBUTION OF VARIOUS PARTS OF THE CAR AT 16/46 MM, FRONT/REAR RIDE HEIGHT, AND MEDIUM DOWNFORCE

COMPONENTS	DRAG		DOWNFORCE		L/D
	CD	%CONTRIB.	CL	% CONTRIB.	
Front wing	0.123	13.2%	0.966	36.9%	7.859
Rear wing	0.297	31.8%	0.899	34.4%	3.029
Underfloor	0.099	10.6%	1.080	41.3%	10.911
Front wheels	0.150	16.0%	-0.038	-1.4%	-0.251
Rear wheels	0.187	20.1%	-0.061	-2.3%	-0.326
Turning vane	0.023	2.4%	-0.020	-0.8%	-0.889
Other	0.055	5.9%	-0.210	-8.0%	-3.793
Total	0.934	100.0%	2.617	100.0%	2.802

LEFT: *[Fig. 7-4] Aero maps for F1-2000. These colour-shaded contour plots show how front and rear axle lift coefficients, the drag coefficient, and the balance change with front and rear ride height.*

TOP RIGHT: *[Fig. 7-5] Peak efficiency occurs at a drag coefficient equivalent to a 331kph top speed.*

RIGHT: *[Fig. 7-6] The wing set-up options for the F1-2000 maintain the aero balance as downforce and the associated drag are increased.*

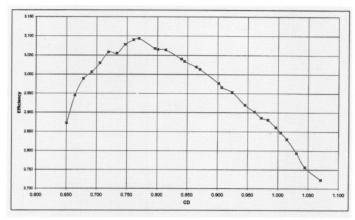

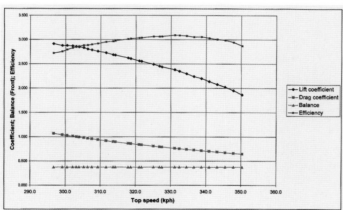

The negative pressure generated on this virtually horizontal surface results in a mainly vertical force and, hence low drag. The next most useful, aerodynamically, is the front wing, also working in ground effect. The rear wing has an efficiency similar to the overall efficiency and is therefore the component that is adjusted to arrive at the desired lift/drag ratio for a given circuit. All the other parts listed—particularly the front and rear wheels—generate lift, not downforce, while making large contributions to the drag. It is not surprising that new under-trays, diffusers, and front and rear wings appear on the cars at regular intervals, the products of the intensive CFD and wind tunnel programmes that all teams carry out all year round.

TABLE 7-2: RANGE OF CL, CD, BALANCE, AND EFFICIENCY FOR THE FERRARI F1-2000

EST. MAX SPEED	CL	CD	BALANCE	EFF.
296.6	2.915	1.070	37.93%	2.724
299.1	2.879	1.044	38.06%	2.757
300.4	2.878	1.030	37.95%	2.794
302.0	2.871	1.014	38.08%	2.831
303.0	2.860	1.004	38.02%	2.848
303.8	2.850	0.996	38.04%	2.861
305.2	2.832	0.983	38.07%	2.881
306.3	2.806	0.972	38.04%	2.886
307.5	2.788	0.961	38.03%	2.902
309.2	2.760	0.945	38.02%	2.920
311.6	2.729	0.924	37.97%	2.954
313.6	2.688	0.906	38.06%	2.966
314.2	2.683	0.901	38.07%	2.977
317.8	2.623	0.870	37.97%	3.014
318.6	2.610	0.864	37.98%	3.021
321.0	2.564	0.845	37.92%	3.035
321.6	2.554	0.840	37.94%	3.041
325.0	2.494	0.814	38.08%	3.065
326.8	2.455	0.801	38.08%	3.066
327.5	2.441	0.796	37.90%	3.068
331.1	2.381	0.769	38.05%	3.094
332.4	2.350	0.760	38.14%	3.091
334.5	2.299	0.747	38.09%	3.079
336.6	2.240	0.733	37.90%	3.056
338.7	2.200	0.719	38.02%	3.059
340.9	2.138	0.705	37.94%	3.031
343.1	2.079	0.691	38.07%	3.007
345.4	2.026	0.678	38.03%	2.989
347.8	1.956	0.664	38.06%	2.946
350.3	1.868	0.650	37.98%	2.873

LEFT: *[Fig. 7-7] The 1.7MW of heat emitted by the cooling and exhaust made visible by its effect on the air disturbed by the car.*

However, the flows around an open-wheel racing car are so complex that no single components can be developed in isolation, each interacting with the others. The front wing tips and the contact patch of the front wheels generate strong vortices that flow downstream, affecting the underfloor flow and the flow into the radiator ducts. The flow over and around the cockpit cavity and around the driver's helmet determines the pressure recovery of the engine intake. The rear wing strongly interacts with the diffuser. The engine exhaust, which is variable, affects the diffuser, if it exhausts under the car, and the rear wing when exhausting from the top surface of the body, as on the F1-2000. The rear wheels affect the under-car flow and the rear wing. Brake cooling is affected by the components ahead and around

the brakes, and they themselves affect the flow under the car. The turning vanes mounted to the front wing end plates, the "barge board" turning vanes, the cockpit rim details, and the scoops and swoops around the rear wheels are all attempts to manage these complex flows (particularly the strong vortices) and maximise positive interactions between elements. It is likely that one of the next areas to be subjected to the aerodynamicists' scrutiny will be the effects of the actual tyre profile, particularly the shoulders of the tyre.

It is not just the simple numbers, indicating lift, lift distribution, drag, and efficiency that must be optimised, equally important is the way these change as the car pitches, heaves, rolls, and yaws to the airstream and the way they are matched to the suspension and vehicle dynamics. These

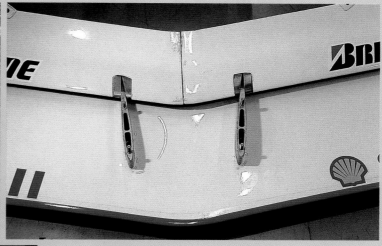

ABOVE LEFT: *The highly loaded front wing works in ground effect, and its characteristics as it moves relative to the ground are critical to the aerodynamic performance of the car. The wing endplates are complex devices that set out to control the vortices shed by the wing tips and interact with the flow around the front wheels.*

ABOVE RIGHT: *Front wing-mounting pillars are aerofoil section and machined internally to reduce unnecessary weight.*

LEFT: *The underside of the front wing. It is paramount to keep the flow attached to the lower surfaces, where there are severe pressure gradients generated by the proximity of the ground. Accurate simulation in the wind tunnel and CFD models are critical to front wing development.*

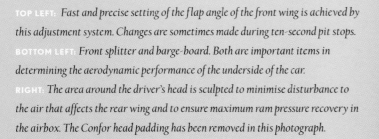

TOP LEFT: *Fast and precise setting of the flap angle of the front wing is achieved by this adjustment system. Changes are sometimes made during ten-second pit stops.*

BOTTOM LEFT: *Front splitter and barge-board. Both are important items in determining the aerodynamic performance of the underside of the car.*

RIGHT: *The area around the driver's head is sculpted to minimise disturbance to the air that affects the rear wing and to ensure maximum ram pressure recovery in the airbox. The Confor head padding has been removed in this photograph.*

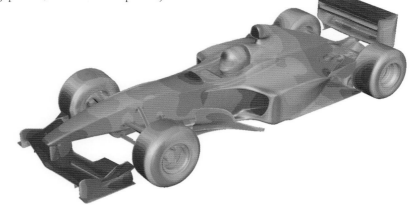

BELOW: *CFD analysis shows surface pressure on the car (red indicates high pressure; blue indicates low pressure).*

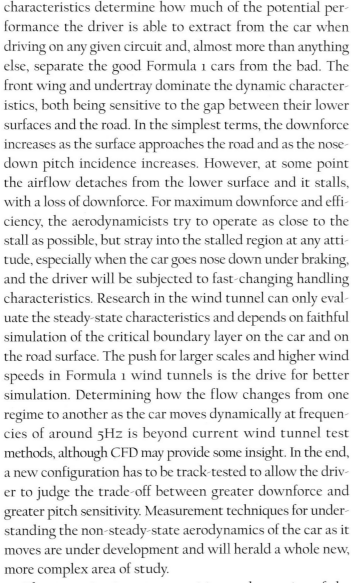

characteristics determine how much of the potential performance the driver is able to extract from the car when driving on any given circuit and, almost more than anything else, separate the good Formula 1 cars from the bad. The front wing and undertray dominate the dynamic characteristics, both being sensitive to the gap between their lower surfaces and the road. In the simplest terms, the downforce increases as the surface approaches the road and as the nose-down pitch incidence increases. However, at some point the airflow detaches from the lower surface and it stalls, with a loss of downforce. For maximum downforce and efficiency, the aerodynamicists try to operate as close to the stall as possible, but stray into the stalled region at any attitude, especially when the car goes nose down under braking, and the driver will be subjected to fast-changing handling characteristics. Research in the wind tunnel can only evaluate the steady-state characteristics and depends on faithful simulation of the critical boundary layer on the car and on the road surface. The push for larger scales and higher wind speeds in Formula 1 wind tunnels is the drive for better simulation. Determining how the flow changes from one regime to another as the car moves dynamically at frequencies of around 5Hz is beyond current wind tunnel test methods, although CFD may provide some insight. In the end, a new configuration has to be track-tested to allow the driver to judge the trade-off between greater downforce and greater pitch sensitivity. Measurement techniques for understanding the non-steady-state aerodynamics of the car as it moves are under development and will herald a whole new, more complex area of study.

The rear wing is not so sensitive to the motion of the car, but it is the element that determines the available range of downforce and efficiency through which the car can be adjusted for different circuits, different conditions (e.g., rain), and different compromises for qualifying and the race.

(See Table 7-2 and Figures 7-5 and 7-6 on page 121.)

Lap simulations, previous experience, and back-to-back testing will determine what compromise between downforce and drag is chosen for any set of circumstances. Qualifying requires whatever setting is quickest over one lap, but race settings are pushed towards the low drag end of the range to ensure that top speeds are adequate to match the critical opposition's and facilitate overtaking. An additional factor is tyre life, as a low-downforce set-up will result in more sliding of the car and, hence, higher tyre temperatures and more wear. This is why front and rear wing settings are often changed on the grid at the last minute. Factors that weigh into making those adjustments include changes in track temperature (which affects tire wear), other weather conditions, and competitors' settings or anticipated race strategy.

A Formula 1 piston engine is overall only around 26 percent fuel efficient (Ref: 7-1), which means that 74 percent of the energy in all the fuel burnt is rejected as heat; i.e., when the engine is producing 800CV, 1.7MW of heat is dissipated to the air passing over and through the car. Telephoto shots of a Formula 1 car on full power, heading for the camera, make visible this heat being rejected into the up-swept turbulent wake of the car by the heat haze around it (Figure 7-7 on page 122). The 95 percent or so of the 800CV produced by the engine that makes it to the rear wheels is used to disturb the air as drag (and a small proportion to make an ear-splitting noise. A large part of this waste heat is in the 800+°C exhaust flow, and the rest is the heat rejected by the

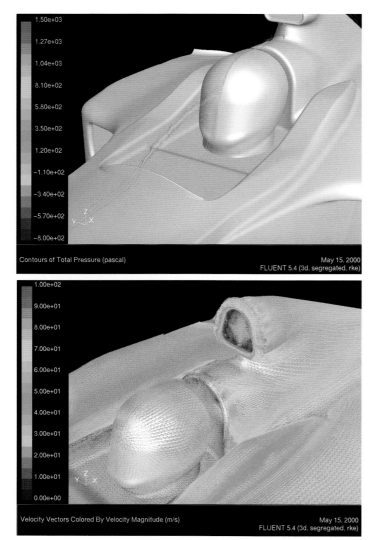

Contours of Total Pressure (pascal)   May 15, 2000
FLUENT 5.4 (3d. segregated. rke)

Velocity Vectors Colored By Velocity Magnitude (m/s)   May 15, 2000
FLUENT 5.4 (3d. segregated. rke)

average around the circuit. The airflow available to take away this heat is derived from the average speed around the circuit and calculated from the airflow through the radiators at a given speed. This is around 15 percent of the airspeed of the car. A balance among the thermal inertia of the systems (weight), the size of the radiators (weight and drag), and their aerodynamic and heat rejection characteristics (drag and downforce, and coolant temperature) is one of the areas where the aerodynamicists must work closely with the engine, transmission, and hydraulic system engineers.

The cooling of the brakes involves similar compromises. The instantaneous heat to the brakes can exceed 1.5MW, but they, too, have thermal inertia. Averaging out the heat input to determine the average cooling rate around the circuit does not completely solve the problem, as great care must be taken to prevent the brake discs exceeding the critical temperature at any time during brake application, at which point oxidation of the carbon-carbon surface is accompanied by an increase in wear rate. Providing cool air to the brake disc and pads and to the caliper itself must be accomplished with the minimum disturbance to the airflow around

and through the wheel and the consequential effects on the downforce. Ideally, all the air should exit through the outside face of the wheel. Airflow in the transverse direction through the wheel is around 20 to 30 percent of the car's airspeed. A range of brake ducts to suit various circuits are developed, with minimalist ones fitted for the short, light runs in qualifying.

engine, transmission, and hydraulic cooling systems via the radiators. The exact balance of exhaust, water, and oil heat rejection depends upon the detail design of the engine and the way the cylinders, pistons, and exhaust ports are cooled. Transmission and hydraulic heat is a result of these components not being 100 percent mechanically efficient; it is wasted horsepower generated by the engine, and so a great deal of R&D effort goes into minimising it.

The mass of the cooled components and the cooling fluids give the systems thermal inertia, and so it is not necessary to provide a cooling capacity capable of instantaneously dissipating the maximum heat rejected at full power, only the

LEFT: CFD analysis of the cockpit region includes surface pressure (bottom) and total pressure contours (top).

BELOW: Right-hand side cooling duct supplies air to the right-hand water radiator. The tank mounted on the side of the duct is the water expansion tank.

ABOVE: *Combined engine oil and gearbox oil radiator on the left-hand side of the car. The space between the intake ducts and the sidepod provides a cool mounting place for electronic black boxes, even if they are vulnerable in an accident.*

ABOVE RIGHT: *Extensive 3-D sculpting of the diffuser and underbody exit maximises the flow under the car.*

RIGHT: *High-downforce rear wing has eight elements. It is supported centrally on the rear impact structure and insulated from the hot exhaust gases.*

8

Brakes, Suspension, and Steering

The first thing any new driver to Formula 1 comments on, whether he has graduated from Formula 3, Formula 3000, CART, or IRL, is how the car stops. The performance of the brakes is difficult to see from outside the car, in spite of the explosion of black dust that is emitted by the cars in the braking zones and the orange glow of the discs visible through the wheels. Still, it is the deceleration generated by the brakes of a Formula 1 car, and just how late the drivers can leave their braking, that most impresses drivers on their first experience. The numbers are impressive too. Figure 8-3 on page 130 illustrates the braking

Figure 8-3 on page 130

LEFT: *The rear suspension is all CFRP, with gold heat insulation to protect it and the vulnerable bonded titanium end fittings from exhaust heat.*

RIGHT: *A view of the front upright and brake. Note the sensor connectors for wheel speed, brake temperatures, and brake disc wear, with spares for test purposes.*

performance of the Ferrari F1-2000 during Michael Schumacher's qualifying lap at Imola in 2000, Imola being one of the circuits that puts the most demand on the brakes. In the figure, the speed of the car around the circuit is plotted, along with the longitudinal acceleration. During the braking phases at the end of each straight, the contributions to the deceleration of the car that come from the aerodynamic drag and the brakes are plotted separately. From the brake contribution, the instantaneous power absorbed by the brakes can be calculated and summed around a lap to give the total energy dissipated per lap. Figure 8-4 on page 130 shows a magnified view of the peak braking zone that starts

at around 4,000 metres around the track; that is, the car brakes for the Rivazza corners, from 302kph down to 109kph in just 2.5 seconds, covering 126 metres in the process.

The peak aerodynamic braking, 1.1g, occurs immediately after the driver lifts off the throttle, and then falls exponentially with speed. Maximum deceleration from the brakes occurs after 0.3 seconds as the brakes heat up to their optimum performance and Schumacher feels for the peak of 3.35g. At this point, overall braking is 4.2g, and more than 1.51MW (2,025hp) is being dissipated in the brakes themselves. By the time he comes off the brakes, 0.41kWh of energy will have been discarded. Around the whole lap, this figure totals

2.55kWh—enough to light a 100-watt light bulb for more than twenty-four hours.

The primary task for the brake designer is to specify a system that is capable of absorbing the power levels required and on average around a lap to be able to dissipate the energy without exceeding critical temperatures in the disc or pad material. Adding thermal capacity and, therefore, mass to the disc and pads is not an option, since it would also add to the unsprung mass. Thus, the disc and pads must absorb virtually all the energy of a single stop, as very little energy will be dissipated into the cooling airstream during the couple of seconds or so that each braking event lasts for. The carbon-fibre-reinforced carbon materials that are now used universally in Formula 1 were developed in the aircraft industry for conditions similar to those of stopping an aircraft during landing—a single hard brake application with little time to dissipate the energy. Almost all the energy of an individual brake application goes into heating the disc and pads up to their peak temperature of around 700°C. Above this temperature, the carbon starts to oxidise (the exact

temperature depends on the material specification) and the wear rate increases. Between brake applications, the discs and pads must cool to a temperature from which the next application does not take them to a level above the critical 700°C, and so on around a lap.

Cooling is achieved by direct transfer to the air collected by the brake ducts and passed to the high-temperature surfaces and to the core of the disc to be pumped centrifugally through radial holes in the disc itself. Heat is also conducted to the caliper, hub, and wheel and from there to the air; care must be taken to not overheat the wheel bearings. A variety of brake duct designs to suit the characteristics of individual circuits design is developed for the car, each optimised to minimise (or assist beneficially) their disturbance to the airflow around the car. The three or four lap runs used for qualifying, when the cars are light on fuel, do not require the same level of brake cooling as the race, and minimalist ducts, if any at all, may be fitted.

The coefficient of friction of carbon on carbon lies in the range 0.3 to 0.5 and depends on both the characteristics of the

BELOW: [Fig. 8-3 and 8-4] As Schumacher brakes for Rivazza at Imola, his deceleration peaks at 4.2g, of which 3.3g is due to the brakes and the remaining 0.9g is drag. Power absorbed by the brakes is 1,510 KW (2,024hp).

RIGHT: French Grand Prix, Magny Cours. Michael Schumacher retired, Rubens Barrichello third. Schumacher's Ferrari suffered a rare engine failure, but the McLarens were dominant in France.

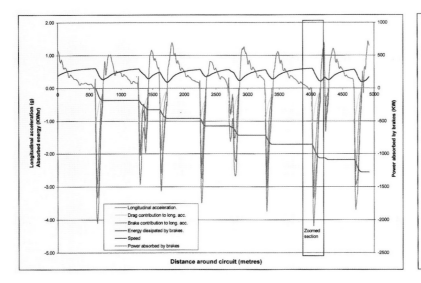

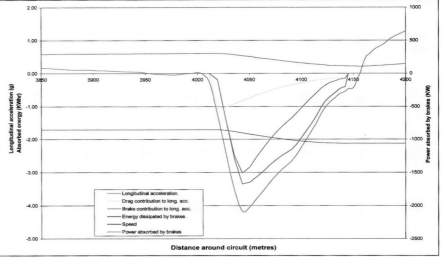

material and the temperature. The carbon-carbon material specification is developed to provide a variety of compromises between initial coefficient of friction when the disc is cool, peak coefficient, and wear rate. The optimum for a given circuit is determined by measurement in testing and the feedback of the driver. The characteristics during the initial and peak braking phases are critical to the stability of the car during these phases.

The maximum clamping loads between the pads and the disc are required when the brakes are applied initially, downforce is a maximum, and the disc and pad material is at its coolest. For optimum braking, the driver should be able to just lock up the wheels under all conditions, but such is the level of downforce and the grip of the tyres that, with-

out power assistance (which is banned), he is not able to do so. Increasing the leverage ratio between the brake pedal and the pad, which includes the hydraulic ratio between the master cylinder and the caliper pistons, to increase the clamping force is an option only up to the point where the pedal travel becomes excessive. The stiffness of the entire brake system determines the maximum leverage ratio possible. The design of the pedal, master cylinders, balance mechanism, hydraulic pipes, brake fluid, and calipers all contribute to the overall system stiffness. The contribution of the U-shaped caliper is particularly important, and FEA analysis has converged designs on the optimum. Material specification ultimately determines this component stiffness and has led firstly to fibre-reinforced aluminium and

LEFT: *Glowing carbon brake discs are visible evidence of the energy being absorbed as the car is slowing by more than 200kph in just three seconds.*

RIGHT: *[Fig. 8-7] The brake balance system is unusual in that the pivot bar is mounted to the "fixed" ends of the master cylinders, instead of the pedal end. The pivot is varied in position to change the balance by a hydraulic cylinder and Moog valve controlled by the driver.*

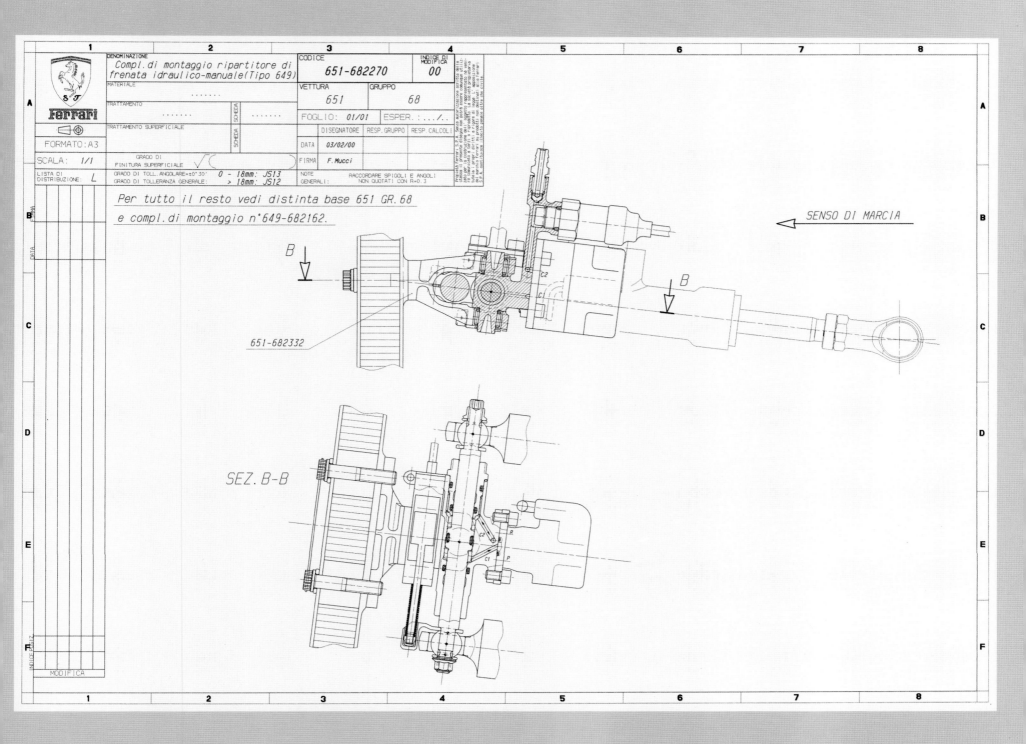

1	2	3	4	5	6	7	8

DENOMINAZIONE
Compl.di montaggio ripartitore di frenata idraulico-manuale(Tipo 649)

CODICE
651-682270

INDICE DI MODIFICA
00

MATERIALE
....

VETTURA
651

GRUPPO
68

TRATTAMENTO
....

FOGLIO: *01/01*   ESPER.:.../..

TRATTAMENTO SUPERFICIALE

	DISEGNATORE	RESP.GRUPPO	RESP.CALCOLI
DATA	*03/02/00*		
FIRMA	*F.Mucci*		

FORMATO: A3

SCALA: *1/1*

GRADO DI FINITURA SUPERFICIALE

LISTA DI DISTRIBUZIONE: *L*

GRADO DI TOLL.ANGOLARE=±0°30'   0 - 18mm: JS13
GRADO DI TOLLERANZA GENERALE: > 18mm: JS12

NOTE GENERALI: RACCORDARE SPIGOLI E ANGOLI NON QUOTATI CON R=0.3

MODIFICA

Per tutto il resto vedi distinta base 651 GR.68
e compl.di montaggio n°649-682162.

B

651-682332

SENSO DI MARCIA

SEZ.B-B

consequently to beryllium-aluminium alloys being used. Aluminium, with a maximum modulus of elasticity of 80Gpa, was imposed, which led to the use of lithium-aluminium alloys to minimise the weight, while keeping within the modulus limit. In 2002, the FIA stipulated that no metallic material with a specific modulus greater than 40Gpa (g/cm³) is permitted on the car and that the calipers must be made from a homogeneous metallic material, halting further expensive developments. Caliper designers had to return to their FEA workstations to hone further weight from the calipers while increasing the stiffness.

The balance of the braking loads generated by the tyres, front to rear, has a significant effect on the stability of the car while braking at the limit, as it determines how much of the tyres' capabilities are left for generating stabilising lateral forces. As the car brakes from high speed, the vertical load distribution, front to rear, varies according to the aerodynamic downforce, which reduces exponentially with speed, and the fore and aft load transfer, which reduces as the maximum braking deceleration falls off as the downforce reduces. From the point of maximum braking, the driver may, depending on his style, be trying to turn the car into the approaching corner. If the car is unstable, this manoeuvre may put the car in a situation where it is beyond his ability to prevent it from spinning. His options are then to brake earlier and less hard or to complete the braking in a straight line and turn in with minimum braking. Adjusting the brake balance to achieve a front bias, thus stabilising the car but reducing braking performance from the optimum, allows the driver to fine-tune the stability to suit his style and to alter it as conditions change. Changing fuel load, tyre performance, track temperature, and rain will all require different optimum brake balance.

Because of the importance of the braking phase to both overall lap time and the ability to overtake other cars, the way

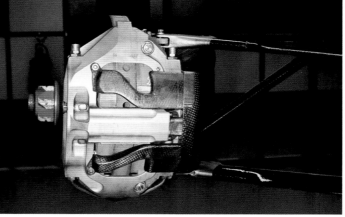

TOP LEFT: *Another view of the front upright and brake. The brake duct feeds air to the pads in the rear-mounted caliper, as well as to the centre of the carbon disc.*

LEFT: *Air is ducted to the pads and pistons of the front caliper to ensure that the brake fluid does not boil.*

RIGHT: *The rear caliper is mounted as low on the upright as possible to position its weight lower.*

in which the brake balance is adjusted has come under close scrutiny of the regulators. By 2000, any means by which the brake balance was adjusted side to side was banned, following McLaren's "fiddle" brake experiment (in which a second brake pedal with a valve to switch from left to right was used to apply a single rear brake). ABS was banned in 1994. Only the driver was permitted to adjust fore and aft brake balance, not a computer control system, and he could do so only while the brakes were not applied. This permitted a powered adjustment system (but no power assistance to the brakes themselves), but even this has now been banned. In 2000, only Ferrari fitted a servo-adjustment system, controlled by driver inputs via a rotary switch and two buttons on the steering wheel. The added complexity of such a system permitted the driver to make fine adjustments to the balance without taking his hands from the wheel and enabled him to tune the car for each corner if he wished. A traditional mechanical system, with a cockpit-mounted control, is too difficult to operate while manoeuvring the car between corners, except on the longer straights.

The Ferrari system mounts the master cylinders on a pivoted bar, such that the pivot is moved by a hydraulic cylinder, controlled by a Moog valve, to alter the ratio of the forces applied by the brake pedal to each cylinder (Figure 8-7 on page 133).

Brake disc temperatures and thickness are measured at all times to monitor performance and wear. With carbon-carbon brake materials, both disc and pads wear at around the same rate, and because the overall volume of the discs is controlled to a maximum of 278mm diameter x 28mm thickness, monitoring wear during a race is necessary. When the disc is worn out, it disintegrates, leading to brake failure. Thinner discs and pads, sometimes with the cooling holes in the disc omitted, are often fitted for qualifying, reducing the overall and unsprung masses.

FERRARI'S TECHNICAL PARTNER FOR BRAKES: BREMBO. Brembo started life in 1961 as a small specialist machine shop. At that time, the only disc brakes available in Italy were imported from the United Kingdom. Recognizing and seizing an opportunity, Brembo started manufacturing disc brakes and was awarded a production contract by Alfa Romeo in 1964. In 1975, Ferrari approached Brembo to develop a brake system to match the performance of Ferrari

Formula 1 cars, and this inevitably led to the company becoming involved more widely in racing.

In 2000, Brembo took over AP Racing, the other main supplier of Formula 1 and high-performance racing brakes. Today Brembo employs more than 3,000 people and has sales of more than €530 million annually.

SUSPENSION AND STEERING.

The main objectives of the suspension system on any car are to control the attitude of the tyre relative to the road surface, to control the vertical force between the tyre and the road, and to transfer all the forces generated by the tyre into the chassis of the car. In performing the latter, the suspension will determine the attitude the chassis takes up when subjected to those forces. On a car that generates aerodynamic downforce by ground effect, the attitude of the aerodynamic surfaces relative to the ground has particular importance: the requirements for optimising that attitude may conflict with the objective of controlling tyre vertical forces, particularly on an uneven road surface.

The steering system allows the driver to modify the slip angle of the tyres to control the horizontal forces generated by them and must work in unison with the suspension. On a Formula 1 car, only the front wheels may be steered.

A wheel and tyre have six degrees of freedom—linear motion along each of the vertical, longitudinal, and lateral axes, and rotation about each axis—and any linkage system to control the six degrees of freedom must have a minimum of six links. The arrangement of these links into the suspension of Formula 1 cars has been established for more than fifty years as top and bottom wishbones, each made up of two links: a steering or toe-control link and a diagonal link to transfer the vertical load to the springing and damping media. The diagonal link that acts in compression is now most favoured. Though structurally less efficient than a link in tension, it

TOP LEFT: *The brake duct for the rear brake must pick up air from between the wheel and the "Coke-bottle" sides of the rear bodywork.*

BELOW LEFT: *The brake balance system can just be glimpsed behind the brake pedal.*

TOP RIGHT: *[Fig. 8-13] The front suspension arrangement. Note the ride-height adjuster operating on the forward anchor point of the short torsion bar spring.*

BELOW RIGHT: *[Fig. 8-14] The rocker operates the short torsion bar spring, the through-rod damper, and the third spring/damper of the front suspension. The upright is fabricated from machined titanium components, in a similar manner to the gearbox case.*

FAR RIGHT: *[Fig. 8-15] The rear suspension arrangement.*

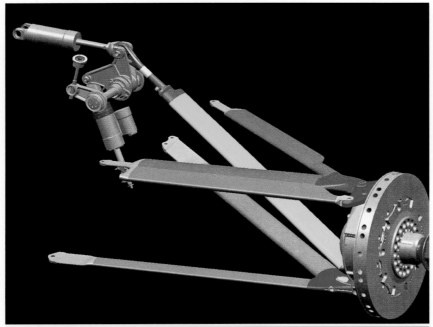

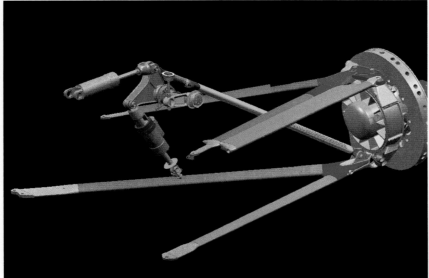

sides of an axle's suspension by levers fixed to the shaft. The third spring permits the stiffness and damping in roll and heave to be partially de-coupled, as this spring/damper only sees deflection when the axle heaves and does not move in roll; the anti-roll spring system achieves the opposite. Thus, the heave properties are the sum of those contributed by the main springs and dampers plus the third spring/damper, while the roll properties are those from the main spring/dampers plus the anti-roll spring. Geometrical characteristics of the push rod and rockers mounted to the shaft allow the designer to build in non-linear characteristics, usually rising rate (the wheel rate increases with compression of the suspension, achieved through linkage geometry), which will be additional to any rising rate characteristics of the springs themselves.

The suspension geometry determines how the tyre is presented to the road under any set of conditions, influencing the tyre contact patch shape and the way the tyre is deflected and, hence, the forces it generates and the critical temperature distribution in the tread area. The geometry also affects the direction of the forces fed into the chassis via

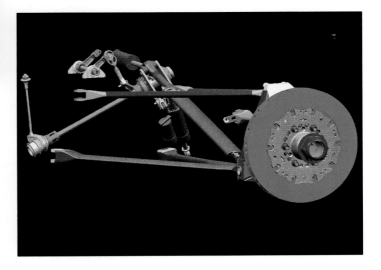

reduces the compression loads in the bottom wishbone of the highly loaded outer wheel when cornering.

The diagonal push rod rotates a shaft via a short lever. All spring, anti-roll bar, and damping forces are fed into this shaft. Current practice, as illustrated in Figures 8-13, 8-14, and 8-15 for the Ferrari F1-2000, is to use the shaft to twist a torsion bar as the primary spring and to operate the dampers, anti-roll bar, and a third spring/damper connecting the two

speed, tractive effort, slip angle, temperature, and, most complex of all, the details of the surface on which it is running. Quasi-steady-state characteristics can now be determined by a combination of analysis, rig testing, and by using the car itself as a tyre dynamometer, but a full understanding of the dynamic effects is farther off. The suspension and steering geometries must take all these effects into account.

Geometries worked out on linkage software mean nothing if the installation and components are not stiff enough. Not only does compliance in the system make nonsense of the kinematics, but the motion generated by parts deflecting under load is undamped and may easily resonate undesirably. Compliance is a trade-off between the stiffness and weight of components. But good design, based on a complete understanding of the loads involved, is the basis of a stiff installation, especially applied to the joints between components. Analysis software developed for road cars, which intentionally have significant compliance for isolation performance, provides suspension designers with the ability to examine kinematics and compliance together. However, the proof of the pudding is in the eating, and many a designer has been surprised at the flexibility of his design when tested under representative loads. Chassis Kinematics and Compliance (K&C) rigs are becoming an essential part of a team's facilities. A complete car can be mounted on the K&C rig, loaded up at the tyre contact patches to represent actual conditions based on track measurements, and the wheel attitudes measured.

The spring stiffness of the front and rear suspensions is determined by the desired compromise between chassis attitude control under aerodynamic and inertia loads as the speed and horizontal accelerations vary and the need for the dampers to move to absorb the energy put into the car by traversing the bumps in the track. Each circuit requires

the links and, hence, the attitude the chassis takes up, which in turn affects the way the tyre is presented to the road. The ability to analyse this complex feedback system has been greatly facilitated by computer simulation and on-track measurement of the actual loads and displacements the suspension experiences under all running conditions. The piece of the equation that is only now being completed is the tyre and its characteristics under all conditions of load,

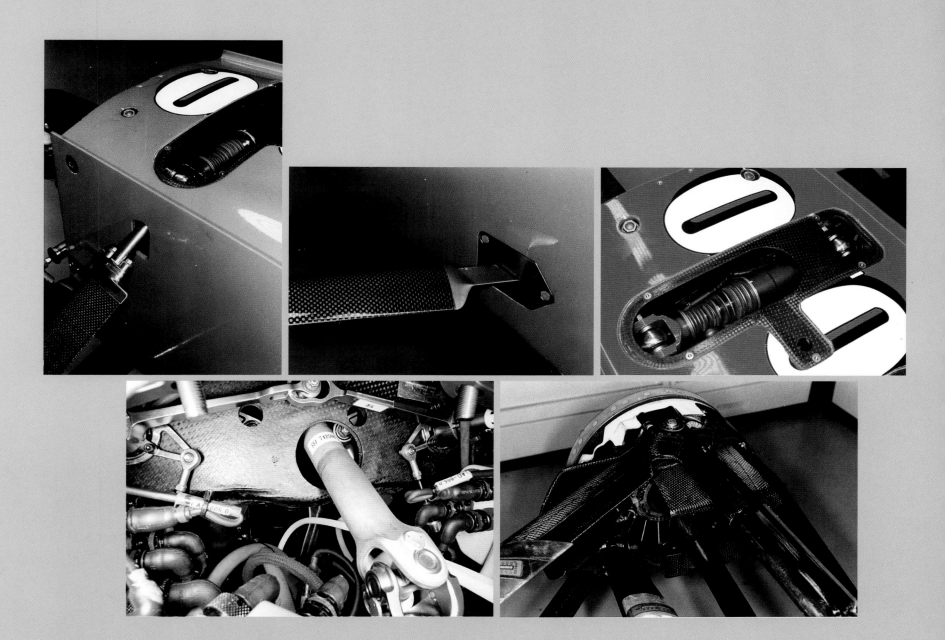

TOP ROW (LEFT TO RIGHT): ▪ *The front suspension push rod operates the third, transverse damper and its Belville washer spring via a rocker.*

▪ *The front suspension inboard pivots are titanium flexures. The small front suspension movement makes this arrangement feasible, and the flexures eliminate friction and provide a stiffer mounting compared to ball joints. This solution is not only effective; it also is extremely elegant.*

▪ *Belville washers provide the springing medium for the third spring at the front.*

BOTTOM ROW (LEFT TO RIGHT): ▪ *The front suspension rockers operate a pair of flexure blades, connected by a roller and slot, to provide anti-roll springing. The front displacement sensors also are driven off the rocker. The steering column uses a large universal joint to connect it to the power steering rack.*

▪ *The rear suspension upright and brake ducting. The upright is a titanium fabrication.*

a different compromise, and each driver has a different personal preference for the way the car responds to driver inputs. The suspension acts as a filter to his inputs, and having done their apprenticeships in karts, many drivers prefer a stiff, responsive suspension. The stiffer the springs, the less the attitude of the car relative to the road will change, making the aerodynamicist's job easier. However, the understanding of pitch stability and dynamic aerodynamic characteristics is increasing, and the compromise with tyre grip, which benefits from a soft spring rate, can be reduced.

The wheel rates of a Formula 1 car are from five to thirty times higher than those of a small road car, which has around twice the mass of the racing car, and so ride frequencies are much higher. The wheel rate is similar in magnitude to the vertical rate of the tyre, and so the two springs in series must be considered together. Because the tyre has very low vertical damping, nearly all the energy from the road must be extracted by the suspension dampers, even though the amplitude of their motion is very small. Although ride quality is almost irrelevant in a Formula 1 car, the control of the dynamic variation in the vertical load at the tyre contact patch is critical to the maximum grip available and the temperature generated in the tyre.

Damper technology is a whole science in itself, involving mechanical and hydraulic analysis and dynamic test rigs. The complete car can be placed on a servo-hydraulic road simulation rig, with additional servo-actuators applying vertical loads to represent aerodynamic downforce. Using measured track profiles, sine sweeps, or white noise inputs, the contact patches are excited appropriately and the response of the suspension and chassis structure is measured. The greatest value of such rigs is to validate simulations, as the dynamic response of a nonrotating tyre is not the same as a rotating one. Also there is a tendency for the aero-load actuators to be imperfect constant load generators and thus extract (or

LEFT: *The rear rocker operates the torsion bar spring and the Sachs through-rod damper (almost completely shielded by heat insulation). The damper is supplied with cooling air from the airbox.*

RIGHT: *The rear suspension third spring and damper. The stack of Belville washers form the springing medium as they are lighter and more compact than a coil spring of equivalent characteristics. The anti-roll bar is not fitted in this picture.*

add) energy from the system in an unrepresentative way, complicating the use of the rig for the development of damper characteristics. Even the warming up of the car components, particularly the dampers, will change the characteristics, leading to a tendency to chase the car as it changes.

CFRP (carbon-fibre-reinforced plastic) is used for the streamline section links and wishbone legs, with bonded-in titanium end fittings. At the front, where wheel movement

is significantly less than at the rear, the inboard ball joints are mostly replaced with flexure pivots to improve stiffness and eliminate stiction and friction. At the rear, ball joints are still used to accommodate the greater angular movement of the joints. Great care is required to protect the CFRP and the bonded joints from the heat of the exhausts and radiator exit air. Insulation and temperature monitoring is universal, particularly around the adhesive joints, with parts being re-tested for strength or discarded if critical temperatures are exceeded. The uprights are either fabricated from CNC-machined sections, in steel or titanium, or more recently, investment-cast and machined in titanium.

the track. For R&D purposes, the loads in all the links may be measured along with hub vertical acceleration, tyre slip angle, and any localised loads, deflections, accelerations, temperatures, or damper hydraulic pressures that the suspension and design engineers may be interested in.

Quite apart from its extensive display and the control input functions on it, the steering wheel also retains its traditional function of being the prime control by which the driver influences the heading of the car. Electro-hydraulic power steering, as fitted to the Ferrari F1-2000, is the normal specification, though the regulations have changed since 2000 such that only hydro-mechanical power steering is permitted, in order to avoid the need for software inspection. The input for the power assistance is the torque in the steering column, measured by a strain gauge torque sensor. A Moog valve controls the pressure across the piston of the hydraulic cylinder in parallel with the conventional rack and pinion steering. The system is monitored and fails to a safe mode. It can also be switched off by the driver, and the assistance characteristics can be selected via a control on the wheel, but only when the car is stationary. The regulations do not permit any other input than steering torque, steering

Great attention to aerodynamic detailing is paid to any part that spans the space between the monocoque and the front wheel. Less critical is the rear suspension, but it still warrants airfoil section links. The FIA was forced to control the extent to which the links could be faired, as aerodynamicists started to exploit them to influence the airflow.

The performance of the suspension is monitored by measuring push rod loads and damper deflections all the time the car runs. Laser ride-height sensors are also fitted to monitor chassis attitude, as tyre deflection is hard to measure on

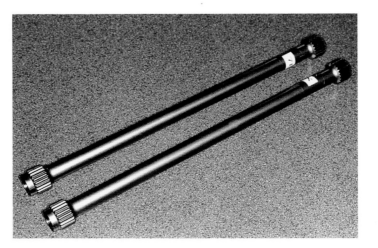

TOP LEFT: *The three components of the rear suspension are the rocker, which also drives the damper; the rocker pivot shaft, which also connects to the torsion bar spring and anti-roll bar; and the fixed mounting for the front end of the torsion bar, incorporating the ride-height adjustment.*

BOTTOM LEFT: *The short double-ended links connect the rocker shaft to the antiroll bar. The long links connect to the ride-height adjuster at the forward end of the torsion bar spring.*

NEAR LEFT: *The rear torsion bar springs*

RIGHT: *By dispensing with adjustable valves and using only aluminium, titanium, and engineering plastics in their construction, the weight of Sachs' F1 through-rod dampers has been reduced from 600gms for a typical four-way adjustable unit to 200gms.*

angle, and car speed, and the system may not do anything other than reduce the physical effort required by the driver to steer the car. The system may not steer the car itself in any way, but the assistance can vary with steer angle and increase with speed.

FERRARI'S TECHNICAL PARTNERS FOR SUSPENSION AND STEERING: ZF SACHS.

Sachs is part of the ZF Group, the third-largest automotive industry supplier in Germany and fifteenth worldwide, with 55,000 employees and an annual turnover of more than €8.5 billion.

Sachs supplies clutches and shock absorbers for a wide

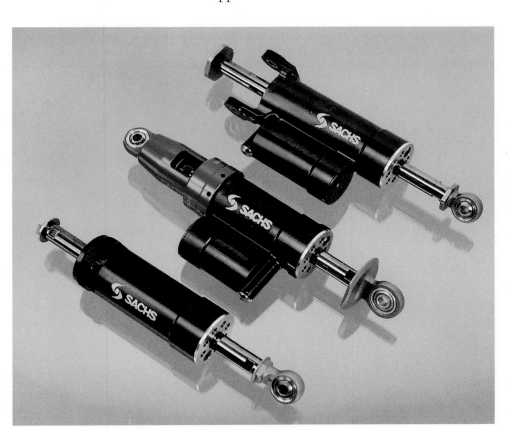

range of vehicles and is active in motor racing in a large number of series around the world. Its initial involvement in Formula 1 was with the Swiss Sauber team, and it has been a partner of Ferrari since 1997, when it was approached to develop a new range of lightweight dampers for its Formula 1 cars.

BBS.

BBS was established in 1971 to manufacture plastic body parts for automobiles. In 1973, it developed a three-piece alloy wheel for racing that was so successful that it transformed the company, and by 1983 BBS was supplying its wheels for road cars.

BBS developed the first forged-magnesium wheel for racing, achieving a weight savings of around 4kg per car.

In 2000, BBS employed 1,000 people and had sales of more than €150 million worldwide.

SKF.

Founded in 1907, the Swedish company SKF developed the world's first self-aligning rolling bearings, from which it has grown into the global leader in ball and roller bearings. Annual turnover is more than 43,000 MSEK (million Swedish kronor), and the group employs 40,000 people worldwide.

SKF's angular-contact wheel hub bearings offer motorsport applications low friction, low weight, and high stiffness, and they are almost universally used in high-performance racing cars. Ferrari's partnership extends beyond bearings, with SKF's expertise in high-specification steels being one area of cooperation.

9

Tyres

*T*he development philosophy of a tyre supplier to any racing series and to Formula 1 in particular is shaped by the competition. If it is the sole supplier, as Bridgestone was in 2000, there is by definition no need to compete. With a guaranteed win in every race, the watching public, all of whom are potential customers of Bridgestone, will take little notice of the make of tyres used, unless their particular hero complains about them and uses the tyres as an excuse for a less-than-expected performance. It is hard to gain good publicity under these conditions

LEFT: *The greatest transport costs of anyone in Formula 1 are borne by the tyre companies, which ship literally thousands of bulky tyres to each race.*

RIGHT: *Rain tyre tread patterns used to be the domain of intuitive designers, but now the channels and grooves are developed using CFD to predict how the water will flow between the tread and the track surface.*

and all too easy to receive bad press. Tyres and aerodynamics so dominate the cornering speed of a racing car, and as a consequence partially determine the speed at the end of the subsequent straight, that they become a major safety issue. All attempts to control speeds through limitations on the design of parts influencing the aerodynamics of the cars have merely produced a temporary hesitation in the continuing trend toward greater downforce. The FIA had introduced a rear tyre width limit of 380mm in 1993, but the tyre competition between Goodyear and Bridgestone had pushed up speed to the extent that the FIA also, controversially, stipulated that tyres must have regulated

circumferential grooves in their treads—three in the front and four in the rear. It took a season for the tyre suppliers to master the new technology, and speeds started to rise again. Proposals to add additional grooves, some transverse, were rejected by the tyre companies on the grounds that full treaded tyres were not practical for the loads involved in Formula 1. The regulation has now, at least temporarily, stabilised, with an additional groove in the front to compensate for the larger-width front tyres, which were developed by Bridgestone as the only way to increase the amount of rubber presented to the track. The FIA also applied a maximum width of 355mm for a front tyre.

Bridgestone's prime considerations in 2000 were safety and cost. Bridgestone has been in Formula 1 since 1997, competing with Goodyear until 1998, and had a large enough database in 1999 and 2000 to be able to play safe. Only four different compounds were used to cover all the circuits with their wide variety of speeds and climates, and tyres were shipped by sea, preventing any last-minute development for a particular race. With Bridgestone as sole tyre supplier and having had fully treaded tyres rejected, the FIA requested that Bridgestone act conservatively with the choice of compounds it fielded, in order to control the escalation of speeds. Without competition, this coincided with Bridgestone's desire to supply safe tyres that did not overheat and blister or wear unduly, and it was happy to comply. That is, until Michelin announced that it would re-enter Formula 1 in 2001.

In the last few races of 2000, Bridgestone started to develop and race more competitive compounds, equally directed towards Ferrari and McLaren, its two prime teams for 2001 and neck and neck in the fight for the championship. No regulation has ever been found that controls compounds, except banning tyre changes during a race and ensuring that the same type of tyres are used for qualifying and the race.

Pit stops have become such a part of the spectacle of Formula 1 and one of the major opportunities for overtaking that no one was ready to ban them. In 1999 and 2000, up until the time that the development for 2001 started, Bridgestone supplied one engineer to each team to monitor tyres, provide liaison, and measure essential tyre parameters, such as temperature and wear. Two compounds were provided as options at each race—a prime and a harder fallback compound, in the event that temperatures or wear turned out to be excessive. Basic data on the tyres' characteristics, measured on flat belt and drum tyre test rigs, were supplied to each team, and they were left to get on with it. Since then, the situation has changed radically, with the relationship between Ferrari and Bridgestone becoming by far the closest between team and tyre supplier in the history of Formula 1.

In 2001, with Michelin working closely with the fast-improving Williams-BMW, Bridgestone responded by increasing the number of engineers assisting the teams and the supply of more detailed information concerning the tyres they were running. Initially the emphasis was as much on a good qualifying performance as on the race, which resulted in some inconsistency during long stints on a set of tyres and occasional blistering.

For 2002, as Michelin had signed up Ferrari's other major competitor, McLaren, Bridgestone was able to focus its efforts on Ferrari, as the customer who offered by far the best chance of beating Michelin. All of Bridgestone's teams had access to the tyres for testing before a race, but there is no doubt that the technical relationship between Ferrari and Bridgestone became very close, with a two-way exchange of data. Race consistency became the focus of tyre development, and Ferrari was sometimes beaten to pole by Michelin's qualifying optimised tyres. This only lost one race to McLaren, at Monaco, where overtaking is almost impossible.

Although 2000 was a year when all the teams had the

LEFT: The four tyres provide the only contact between car and track and generate all the forces for controlling and stabilising it.

RIGHT: The introduction of grooved tyres, to limit cornering and braking performance, created controversy around tread wear—at what point does a grooved tyre become a slick? The FIA and the tyre companies have cooperated to create a workable regulation.

same choice of tyres available to them for each race, Ferrari's ability to select the best ones and then to get more out of them than the opposition was a major contribution to its success. Not only did it use the stability of a period when there was only one tyre supplier to develop its simulation technologies, Ferrari also had almost unlimited testing at Fiorano and Mugello.

Racing tyre engineer Kees van de Grint has worked for Bridgestone for eighteen years and has known and worked with Michael Schumacher since his karting and Formula 3 days. "Ferrari's simulation techniques are ahead of the others," van de Grint says, "but track-testing is still the main way we develop tyres. The ratio between science and trial and error is around 40/60. We can make quite good predictions about compounds, but can only forecast trends for different tyre constructions, not absolute values.

"There is no substitute for tyre testing on actual GP circuits, but Ferrari's approach and the amount of testing is most valuable when we cannot use race circuits, and Schumacher is always available when we need him. Bridgestone has cooperated with Ferrari's in-house test track at Fiorano to install computer-controlled water-spraying facilities, so that wet-tyre testing can take place

all the year round under precise and repeatable conditions.

"The driver is still an important way of assessing tyres. He can report trends over several laps, and he is able to feel things we cannot yet measure, such as a tyre coming back after the initial fall-off in performance from new. Track-testing does not always produce the expected result. Currently, we try and maintain the car and the driver as constants, not adapting them to a new tyre. We are rethinking this, as it may be a mistaken approach."

Bridgestone is not alone in finding that tyre construction changes do not always bring the expected results. The interactions between the tyre characteristics, the suspension, the aerodynamics, and the chassis itself and the way they affect tyre temperature, wear, stability, and grip are just too complex to be unravelled by track-testing. Ferrari and Bridgestone have recognised the need to step back and take a more fundamental and perhaps broader approach to research and development, away from day-to-day racing.

Tyres may just be "round and black" to many people who follow motor racing, but they are still one of the major factors dominating the performance of a car. They and the way in which they work with the chassis are also technologies where there is still plenty of scope for further performance gains, as research and development unravels the mysteries of these complex, highly stressed and elastic devices. Ferrari and Bridgestone have recognised this to an extent that has not occurred before, and their partnership is likely to have a significant influence in the design of Ferrari's Formula 1 cars during the coming years. The future is likely to see the relationship strengthen, with an increasing technical exchange and understanding of chassis/tyre requirements. The fruits of such R&D also are likely to make a big contribution to performance, as one of the last "black art" areas of racing becomes a science in a combination of car and tyre that is already dominant.

The only factor that could seriously affect this is the trend in more and more racing series towards single suppliers of "specification" tyres. Whether this will ever reach Formula 1 as a means of reducing costs and evening out the competition for the two championships—drivers' and manufacturers'—remains to be seen.

FERRARI'S TECHNICAL PARTNER FOR TYRES: BRIDGESTONE.

Bridgestone was founded by Shojiro and Tokujiro Ishibashi when they inherited a small family-run clothing company in 1906, on the southern Japanese island of Kyushu. In order to expand the business, they began making traditional Japanese footwear. It was not until the 1920s that they began to put rubber soles on the shoes, but this led them to expand into other rubber products, notably tyres.

In 1931, they played around with the English translation of their name—"ishi" means stone and "bashi" means bridge—and they came up with a new name for the company: Bridgestone. Expansion in the 1930s was enormous, as Japanese industry boomed and expanded its empire in Asia.

As soon as World War II ended, Bridgestone started rebuilding, initially making bicycles—a huge market at the time—but in the early 1950s the company entered into a technical agreement with Goodyear and began to make tyres once again. The Japanese car boom of the 1970s turned Bridgestone into a vast company, and in the early 1980s it began to expand worldwide. In 1983, it bought a Firestone factory in Tennessee and five years later outbid Pirelli to buy the entire Firestone company for $2.6 billion.

Bridgestone is a major producer of specialist tyres, with sales in the airline business and in the heavy equipment sector. The company also is involved in sporting goods and building materials, including roofing, industrial textiles, conveyor belts, fabrics, hoses, and even bicycles.

Tyres may just be "round and black" to many people who follow motor racing, but they are still one of the major factors dominating the performance of a car.

It has research and development centres in Akron, Ohio, in the United States; at Castel Romano, outside Rome; Italy; and at Kodaira in Japan. There are also two Bridgestone test tracks at Kuroiso (to the north of Tokyo) and at Shibetsu on Japan's northern island of Hokkaido.

The company has a strong tradition in motorsport, dating back to the first races in Japan in 1963. It started competing in Japan's top single-seater series when it was established in 1973 (which has been known as Formula 2000, Formula 2, Formula 3000, and now Formula Nippon). Bridgestone has proved to be the dominant force, despite being involved in a lively three-way battle with Sumitomo Rubber Industries (which has produced Dunlop tyres in Japan since 1984) and Yokohama.

In parallel, Firestone had opened a European research centre in Brentford, Middlesex, and in 1966 entered Grand Prix racing with Ferrari, Lotus, and McLaren. In the course of the six years that followed, Firestone won forty-nine Grand Prix victories and three World Championships (1968, '70, and '72).

In 1976, Bridgestone drove Goodyear out of the international karting markets with Martin Hines and Mike Wilson leading the way. Before long Bridgestone dominated the karting world—and still does.

Michelin entered European F2 in 1982, and for the next four seasons the two companies fought a tyre war in F2 and then F3000. In 1986, however, the FIA decided that F3000 should be a one-tyre formula and awarded the contract to Avon. In the 1980s and early 1990s, Bridgestone dominated F2 and F3000 in Japan, winning six titles. The company continued to dominate kart racing. In the late 1980s, the company entered touring car racing in Europe with AMG Motorsport in the German Touring Car Championship. This led to winning the 1992, 1994, and 1995 titles.

The company had long wanted to enter Grand Prix racing, but the Firestone takeover meant that no money was available for the programme. In 1989, the company began testing F1-spec tyres, and it continued until mid-1994. In 1996, Bridgestone announced that it would be entering F1 with the Arrows team. After some impressive performances in 1997, top teams McLaren and Benetton switched to Bridgestone in 1998, and the Japanese company won its first World, Championship with McLaren.

At the end of 1998, Goodyear withdrew from F1, leaving Bridgestone as the sole supplier in Grand Prix racing until 2001, when Michelin re-entered Formula 1 with Williams-BMW. In 2002, with Michelin adding McLaren to its armoury, Bridgestone and Ferrari strengthened its partnership, both commercially and technically, to mount their challenge.

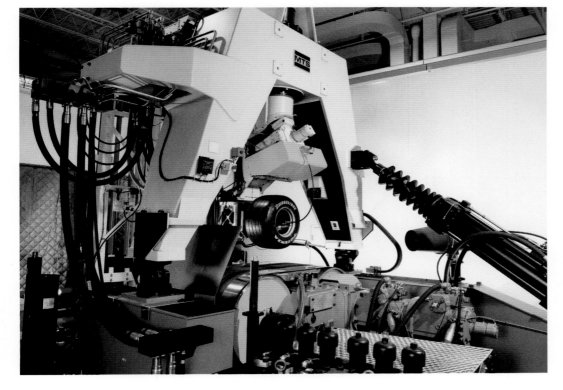

10

Fuel and Lubricants

*T*he turbo-engine era in Formula 1, in the mid-1980s, brought *the fuel companies involved in the sport to the forefront of engine development. As these companies worked to produce high-energy fuels for these (reputedly) 1,000bhp per litre qualifying time bombs and carefully formulated race fuels that enabled the engines to survive a race distance on a reasonably light fuel load (achieving low fuel consumption means running the engine as lean as possible, with the associated increased temperatures), the talk in the paddock was*

LEFT: *Ferrari and Shell's partnership extends beyond marketing. Shell experts attend every test and race and provide analysis of fuel and oil whenever the cars run.*

RIGHT: *A Shell technician prepares to analyse a fuel sample.*

more of fuels than of rpm. Some of these fuels exhibited doubtful environmental properties, and the FIA was forced to act to control the image of Formula 1. By the time they were banned, they also had been applied to the 3.5-liter normally aspirated engines that replaced the turbos, pushing the rate of power development to levels not then possible through normal mechanical means.

The first paragraph of Article 19, the technical regulation governing the composition of the fuel, clearly sets out the objective:
The purpose of this Article is to ensure that the fuel used in Formula One is petrol as this term is generally understood.
The next nine subclauses define the terminology, the prop-

erties of the formulated fuel, its composition, and checking test methodology, and they state that it will meet the European Fuel Directive 98/70/EC, in 2000, and be brought in line with the Final Directive for 2005, as soon as it becomes defined. No other regulation in Formula 1 is quite so specific. However, it also states that any fuel that is formulated with the objectives of suiting advanced passenger car engines, reduced emissions, better fuel consumption, or involving advanced refinery techniques will be permitted.

In terms of controlling power output, the most important limits are on octane number (102RON maximum), which limits compression ratio, oxygen content and the types of oxygenates permitted, and the energy content of the fuel. The fuels

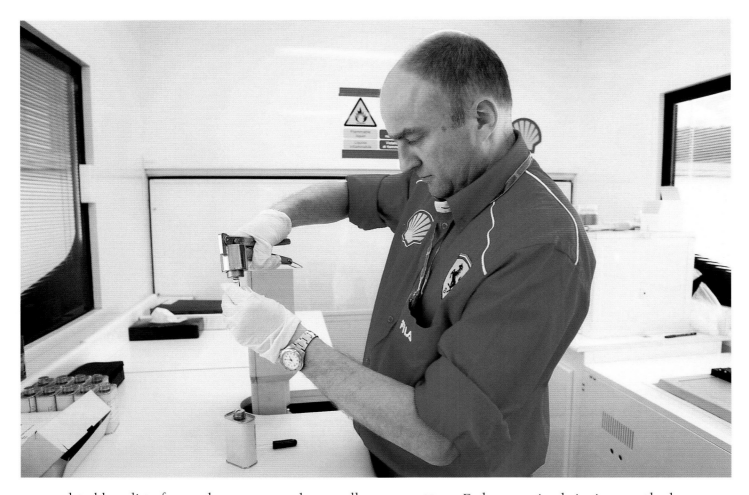

are regulated by a list of around 200 compounds normally found in commercial fuels, which must form 95 percent of the fuel. In addition, the fuel chemists have around 5 percent freedom in the choice of hydrocarbons they may select from outside this list. Thus armed, they set out to determine what formulations suit a given engine, depending on its characteristics, and how power may be traded against fuel consumption to provide the strategists a choice for a given race.

Shell, Ferrari's fuel and lubricants partner, maintains an office in the Gestione Sportiva at Maranello, enabling its engineers and chemists to work as an integral part of the design and devel-

opment team. Each new engine design is run on the dynamometer on a matrix of fuels to determine its "appetite," that is, the trade-off between power and economy. Around thirty different formulations may be tested in a year, and these tests narrow the choice to four or five fuels for specific circuits and chosen strategies. Shell is able to model the performance of each hydrocarbon component in a fuel using engine parameters provided by Ferrari to predict the power generated to better than 0.5 percent. Samples of race fuels are sent to the FIA for approval by chemical analysis, according to methods specified in the regulations and "fingerprinting" by gas chromatography,

LEFT: *Shell's mobile F1 laboratory permits on-the-spot analysis of fuel and oils.*
RIGHT: *The FIA's tightly controlled fuel specification requires rigorous monitoring of fuel to ensure it meets the regulation at all times.*

so that they may be checked at a race that the fuel actually used during a GP event is one that has already been approved as conforming to the regulations.

Ferrari's Formula 1 engines would be quite happy running on fuel available from any roadside garage, and any petrol-engine road car would be happy on the fuel supplied for racing. It is lead free and low in sulphur.

The same can almost be said of the lubricants, though in this case the compromises between road and race applications are somewhat different. Extended protection is not the goal, but greater mechanical efficiency is: it has been possible to liberate 20 to 30 horsepower through lubricants alone. The base oil used in the race engine is very similar to that used in the top-tier Shell Helix oils as sold in garages, but its viscosity is optimised for the higher engine temperatures and loads experienced by the lubricant. The oil is used as the prime means of cooling the pistons, sprayed from jets onto their undersides, which run at temperatures not far short of their softening point. The peak load case for the oil is the surface between the cams and the finger followers, where wear must be controlled. The viscosity versus temperature and load are key characteristics of a racing oil. The trend towards higher engine coolant temperatures,

achieved by running the water system at higher pressure to reduce the size and aerodynamic influence of the radiators, has put an even greater heat load onto the oil.

Deposit control, via detergents in the oil, is less important in a racing engine than in a road car engine, as the design life between major overhauls is only around 350 to 400km, albeit at much higher engine speed. Foaming of the oil has a major influence on the ability to withstand the high loads and on the cooling performance, and it must be minimised. The required characteristics are determined by the additive package and are the product of continuous research. The transmission oil has two prime requirements: to reduce friction in the highly loaded gears and bearings and to remove the heat generated by that friction, taking it away from the loaded surfaces and transferring it to the radiator cooling surfaces. Churning of the oil by the gears may generate additional heat, and minimising this comes from close cooperation between the gearbox designer and the oil supplier.

FERRARI'S TECHNICAL PARTNER FOR FUELS AND LUBRICANTS: SHELL.

Shell's association with Ferrari goes back a long way. In 1927, Enzo Ferrari was racing Alfa Romeo 6C 1500 sports cars, using Shell products, and he continued to do so when Scuderia Ferrari became the racing department of Alfa Romeo in 1929. When Ferrari became independent from Alfa in 1939 and commenced racing cars carrying his own name, he maintained his relationship with Shell. In 1951, Ferrari and Shell gained their first GP win together at Silverstone and World Championships in 1952 and 1953.

The association continued until 1973 and was renewed in 1996. In this latest association, Shell has made Formula 1 and its partnership with Ferrari the focus of its marketing of road car products—Optimax and V-Power fuels, and Helix oils.

ured. Intimate knowledge of the metallurgy of Ferrari's engine and transmission enables the component that is wearing excessively to be traced. These forensic laboratory techniques have prevented premature engine failure on more than one occasion.

Shell brings the full resources of its global enterprise to the partnership. With 2,500 technical staff worldwide and twenty-five refineries, it is able to develop fuels and lubricants and select individual components to formulate these products, from within its own resources. Shell has gained the trust of the Ferrari designers to the extent that they are able to influence hardware design. Hardware and fluids are designed together such that the sum of the two is greater than the sum of the parts.

Around 220,000 litres of fuel and 40,000kg of lubricants are used in the Formula 1 programme each year, the majority in testing. For overseas races, Shell ships 10.5 tonnes of fuel and 1.5 tonnes of oil for the event. In return for this technical and commercial commitment, Shell's technical staff gains racing experience and develops the skills needed to work in a harsh, demanding environment against the clock, but the main advantage is in the actual product. It is true that the fuel available in Shell petrol stations all around the world is a direct offshoot of Formula 1 fuel. The same is true for the oils, as each member of Shell's Formula 1 team contributes to the development of road car products as well as the Formula 1 operation. Of course, the yellow seashell sign sits well alongside Ferrari's logo, and the association provides real impetus to Shell's marketing campaign.

Shell's relationship with Ferrari, however, is not one that is solely marketing based. The technical involvement with Ferrari's engine design and development department is probably the greatest of any fuel company's in Formula 1. Shell engineers and chemists are an integral part of the research and development programme. They have an office at Maranello, and they are on-site for the testing of all new fuels and lubricants on engines, carried out on current and development V-10s, at Ferrari. Shell brings a mobile technical centre to the circuits, the "Track Lab," where fuel and lubricant analysis can be carried out.

At a typical race weekend, forty samples of fuel may be analysed to ensure that they conform to the approved and "fingerprinted" samples analysed by the FIA and have not been contaminated in any way. In addition, forty samples of lubricants are taken and analysed for wear-metal particles. These samples are taken after every test or practice session or engine change, and the amount of different metals (e.g., iron, titanium, vanadium, silver, and lead) in the oil is meas-

11

Systems

Hydraulics, Electrics, and Electronics

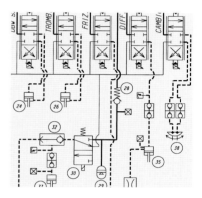

Several of the control systems on the car require a hydraulics power supply to meet the performance specification in terms of force levels and frequency response. Having installed a hydraulic system, it makes sense to use it for control systems that might not demand hydraulics; the hydraulic system is lighter than electrical systems, so using the hydraulic system and avoiding the need for a larger alternator and battery results in lower weight. As a result, there are nine systems connected to the hydraulic supply, as shown in Figure 11-3 on page 158.

as shown in Figure 11-3 on page 158.

LEFT: *The banking at Indianapolis is unique among current GP tracks but did not pose serious problems for the drivers or the engineers setting up the cars. Using computer simulations, teams developed set-ups for banked corners before they had run on the track.*

RIGHT: *A detail of the F1-2000 hydraulic system schematic.*

Items 1 to 9 comprise the 200 bar hydraulic power supply itself.

HYDRAULIC POWER SUPPLY.

The Abex variable-displacement swash-plate pump (1) is driven by the right-hand auxiliary drive on the engine. The pump, developed for use on commercial and military aircraft, has its own internal control system that alters the swash-plate angle to vary the displaced volume per revolution whilst maintaining the desired system pressure. The model fitted to the Ferrari has a maximum displacement of 2.5cc per revolution and, driven at 71.5 percent engine speed, is capable of delivering 10.7 litres per minute at 6,000rpm (the

minimum rpm experienced at Monaco) and a maximum of 32.2 litres per minute at 18,000rpm.

The flow demands of the system are determined by the peak flows of the individual systems, and the lowest engine rpm at which the maximum demand can occur. The sum of the maximum duty flows of each of the eight Moog Series 30 electro-hydraulic servo valves (14, 17, 21, 23, 25, 27, 34, 37) equates to 27.3lpm, plus their tare flows. The tare flow is the continuous internal flow of the valve's hydraulic amplifier and is somewhere between 0.25 and 0.35lpm per valve, depending on valve frequency response. This equates to around 2.5lpm for all eight valves, adding up to a maximum potential flow

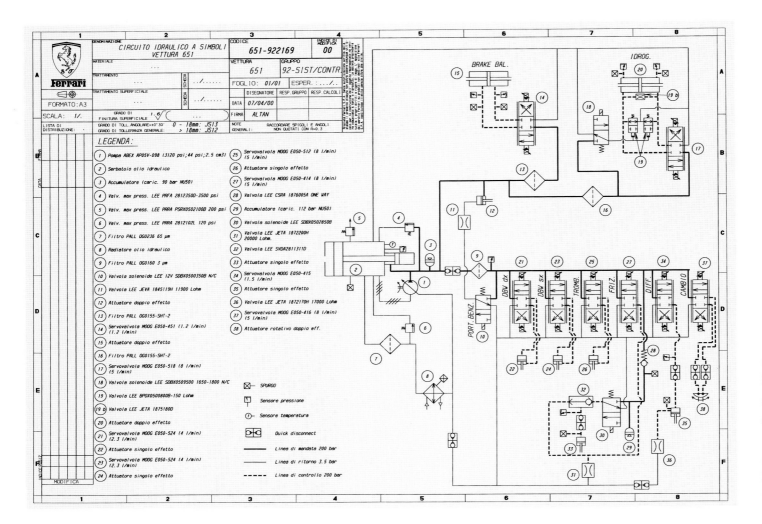

LEFT: *[Fig. 11-3] The schematic of the hydraulic system. Please refer to the text for a detailed description of each subsystem.*

RIGHT: *The refuelling flap is opened by a hydraulic cylinder when the pit lane speed limiter is operated.*

TOP RIGHT: *The right side of the gearbox shows the three hydraulic actuators sticking out of the front, ready to connect into the engine. These control the throttles and trumpets. The hydraulic manifold, Moog valves, and connector box for the rear end of the car are mounted on the side of the gear case.*

for the whole system of 29.8lpm. If the driver works the steering hard while stabbing at the throttles and changes gear, it is possible that the flow demands could reach somewhere near the maximum at almost 30lpm. This rather wild driving is most likely to occur coming out of a slow corner, when engine rpm is at its lowest and the pump can only supply 10lpm. Fortunately, these actions are unlikely to last for long (the car would end up in the barriers if they did!), and so the peak flow demand can be met from the accumulator (3).

The pump and accumulator sizes are determined by the peak and mean flow demands and the engine rpm at which they occur. The other critical period for the hydraulics is at the start. Approaching the start line on the warm-up lap, the driver exercises all the hydraulic systems while accelerating hard and manoeuvring sharply to warm up his tyres, whilst travelling at low speeds. It is essential to maintain engine rpm to ensure the clutch and gear-selection system perform correctly at the start.

If a constant flow pump were used, such as a gear pump, the power consumption at peak rpm (32lpm) would consume around 16hp. By employing a variable displacement pump when running at near maximum speeds in a straight line (i.e., when maximum power is needed), the flow demands are low, the pump reduces its flow, and, hence, power consumption is as little as 3 or 4hp. Heat input to the hydraulic oil also is reduced by this measure.

The pump draws oil from a pressurised reservoir (item 2). This is maintained at 3.5 bar (the increased pressure at the inlet to the pump prevents cavitation occurring at maxi-

mum flow rate) by a large-diameter piston connected to a small-diameter piston that is pressurised by the 200 bar system pressure. Using a sealed reservoir system minimises the volume and, hence, the weight of fluid carried. The volume must be enough to fill the accumulator and the extended internal volume of the single-acting actuators (clutch and differential), but does not have to accommodate either surge due to horizontal g-forces or de-aeration. All the air must be purged from the entire system (there are numerous bleed points—*spurgo*—around the system), as otherwise it would emulsify the hydraulic fluid and reduce the control performance due to "spongy" fluid. This closed-circuit system is similar to that used on military aircraft, but is complicated for an installation that must be overhauled frequently. Quick-release couplings at essential joints, such as those between chassis, engine, and gearbox, allow the system to be broken without loss or contamination of fluid or inclusion of air. The benefit is reduced weight.

Pressurised fluid is filtered (9 for the systems at the rear, 13 and 16 for those at the front), and return oil is cooled (8) and filtered (7). The cooler and return lines are protected from a blocked filter by a pressure relief valve (PRV; 6). Further PRVs protect the pressure side of the system (4) and the

reservoir (5). Pressures and temperatures are measured at a number of points in the system. Pressurised fluid is supplied to each of the control systems, the effective working pressure being 200 bar minus the return line pressure of 3.5 bar, i.e., 196.5 bar or 2,890 psi.

FUEL FILLER FLAP.

The first of the systems in Figure 11-1 is for the actuation of the fuel filler flap, in some ways a surprising application for hydraulics. The three-way solenoid valve (10) is energised when the driver engages the pit lane speed limiter. The double-acting actuator (12) is pressurised by system pressure to the closed position. When the valve is opened, fluid acts on the larger diameter of the hydraulic cylinder and opens the flap. Speed of actuation is controlled by the flow restrictor (11). Opening of the flap when the speed limiter is engaged is mandatory, as a means of signalling that the limiter is in use and not being used as a form of traction control out on the circuit.

BRAKE BALANCE.

The brake balance is adjusted hydraulically by a double-acting cylinder (15), controlled by a Moog valve (14). The way this works is illustrated in chapter 8 and is again an unusual application of servo-hydraulics on a Formula 1 car. The driver's need to adjust balance at the touch of a button justifies the complication.

POWER STEERING.

The power steering is a pressure-control system, modulated by the Moog flow control valve (17) and a flow restrictor (19b). The pressures of each side of the steering actuator piston (20) depend on the flow rate through the restrictor. The pressures are measured and fed back to the control algorithm along with the steering torque, measured by a torque sensor on the steering column.

The system is de-activated in the event of hydraulic, electric, or electronic system failures by a solenoid valve (18), which pressurises two pressure-activated valves (19), short-circuiting the flow across the actuator. The system is normally in the non-powered safe mode and is only activated when the controller energises the solenoid valve for powered mode, that is, when the controller is functioning correctly.

THROTTLES AND TRUMPETS.

Three similar systems, comprising Moog valves controlling double-acting actuators with position feedback, are used for the throttles (21 and 22 for the right-hand cylinder bank, and 23 and 24 for the left-hand bank) and the variable-length trumpets (25 and 26). The very high response required to operate the trumpets fast enough as engine rpm varies, particularly during gear changes, necessitates more than twice the flow rate of one set of throttles.

CLUTCH.

The clutch actuation system uses a Moog valve (27) to control the pressure in the slave cylinder (33) by regulating the flow through a flow restrictor (31); the pressure in the circuit and, therefore, the load on the clutch withdrawal mechanism are fed back to the control algorithm. The position of the actuator is also fed back, so that the take-up point is known and clutch wear is compensated for.

There is a parallel circuit that will open the clutch to provide a "neutral" to enable the car to be pushed away from the track when stranded, as required by the regulations. The "neutral" button energises a solenoid valve (30), isolated from the primary circuit by a non-return valve (32), which connects the clutch slave cylinder to an accumulator (29) to provide the required fifteen minutes minimum. The accumulator is charged from the pressure supply via a non-return valve (28).

RIGHT: *[Fig. 11-6] The steering wheel provides the driver with the majority of control inputs and display functions. Its buttons, knobs, lights, and screens are all configurable in software, and their function may vary from event to event. The wheel connects to the car network via an eight-pin connector in the centre of the quick-release mechanism.*

FAR RIGHT: *[Fig. 11-7] The back of the wheel displays the gearshift paddles (top), pivoting on the centreline, and the two separate clutch paddles. The drilled ring is the sleeve for operating the quick-release mechanism.*

CONTROLS.

Computerised systems have brought with them a simplification of the displays for the driver's information and a significant complication of his control inputs. Apart from the throttle and brake pedals, all information and control inputs necessary to drive the car are incorporated into the Ferrari F1-2000's steering wheel. It is connected via a quick-release attachment, which incorporates a power and data electrical plug linking the microprocessor in the wheel to the Controller Area Network (CAN). Subsidiary controls, those that the driver does not need to operate while driving at the limit, are sited in the left-hand side of the cockpit, down by his thigh. They, too, are connected to the network.

Apart from its prime purpose of providing steering inputs, the two most important controls on the Momo steering wheel are the gear change and clutch paddles mounted behind it (Figures 11-6 and 11-7). The upper paddle is a swinging beam, either side of which can be pulled towards the driver with his fingertips to select either a higher or a lower gear ratio: right-hand side for a higher gear and left-

GEAR CHANGE.

A Moog valve (37) controls the gear-selection barrel actuator (38) with position feedback. The double-acting actuator is a vane-type rotary actuator.

Hydraulic systems on Formula 1 cars are often blamed for failures to finish races. Whether the failures are actually hydraulic failures or sensing/electronic/software failures is not normally stated. The banes of hydraulic systems are contamination and leaks, both prevalent in a system that is opened frequently due to the need to service either the system or the vehicle it is installed on—as with a Formula 1 car. Ferrari has designed a sealed closed-circuit system with filters protecting the various valves that are vulnerable to dirt in the hydraulic fluid.

hand side for a down change. Once the driver has triggered the gear change, the entire process is controlled by the computer without further intervention by the driver. Clutch, throttles, ignition cut, and selector barrel are synchronised to achieve up changes with the minimum loss of power to the rear wheels and down changes that disturb the rear of the car as little as possible with sudden torque pulses to the rear wheels.

Either of the two lower paddles operate the clutch, which the driver only needs to use to get the car rolling at the start or on leaving the pits. Because the paddles operate position sensors and there is none of the load feedback he would get if operating a mechanically linked clutch pedal, it would be difficult for him to determine the clutch take-up point, as it varies with wear, temperature, etc. The take-up point is monitored by software each time the clutch is operated, and the position of the paddles at which it occurs is maintained regardless of wear. All the driver must do is learn that position such that he can modulate the clutch engagement precisely at the start of the race. Since the Spanish GP in 2001, the computer controls the entire start sequence and all the driver must do is tell it when to go! as the start lights change.

The Ferrari's steering wheel presents to the driver a potentially bewildering array of three LCD displays, two LED arrays and twenty-one other LEDs, ten push buttons, and six rotary switches (Figure 11-8). Each display or control input is software configurable; that is, they can all be assigned to any task desired. The configuration described below represents the one most commonly used. It is easy to imagine the potential confusion for the driver if assignments were changed too often!

The two red displays at the top of the wheel provide a sequence of LEDs that light up sequentially as the rpm nears the gear-change point, giving the driver a guide as to when

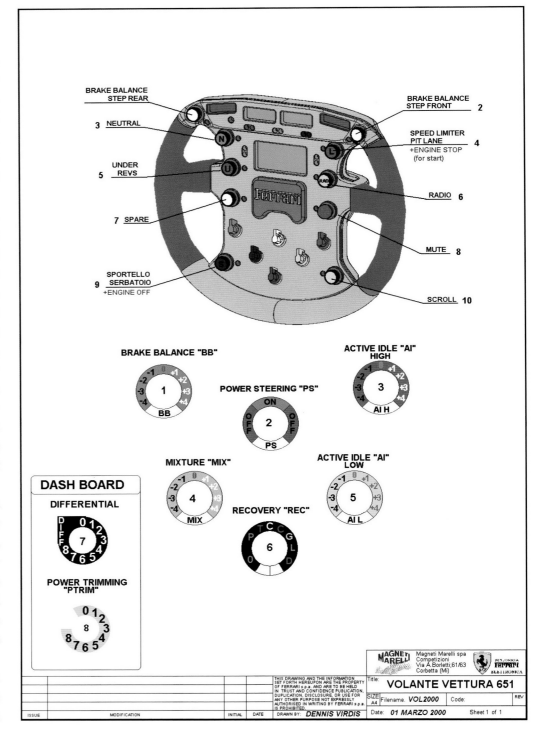

to change. Between them are two LCD displays, the left one displaying sector timing, triggered by a transponder crossing embedded wires in the track (this is fitted to all cars as part of the TAG-Heuer timing system) and the right one displaying car speed. With these two displays, the driver can monitor his performance at points around the track; particularly in qualifying, he is able to determine whether a fast lap is worth finishing to set a quicker time or whether it is better to abandon it and save the tyres.

The large central LCD display shows rpm, gear engaged, engine water and oil temperatures, engine oil pressure, and tyre temperatures—selected by the "Scroll" button (10).

Each button has an LED light beside it to indicate to the driver that the selected function has been activated successfully. Paired LEDs under the two upper LCDs are marshalling lights, triggered by Race Control when red, yellow, or blue flags are displayed. The paired LEDs on either side of the central LCD are warnings to the driver that some parameter is out of limits, which he can then investigate by scrolling the display to determine which one.

The functions of the buttons and rotary switches are as follows:

LEFT: *[Fig. 11-8] Magneti Marelli fits numerous controls and displays into the Momo steering wheel. Please refer to the text for their assigned functions.*

RIGHT: *[Fig. 11-9] The console down by the driver's left thigh houses controls for less critical functions that can be operated when the driver is able to take one hand from the wheel to make the inputs.*

BUTTONS

"Brake balance—Step rear" Moves the brake balance one step to the rear.

"Brake balance—Step front" Moves the brake balance one step to the front.

The above buttons allow the driver to set up brake balance adjustments for a corner or while braking for a corner without removing either hand from the wheel. Larger changes are made via rotary switch 1 (see page 164).

"Neutral" Selects neutral in the gearbox. This function is different from FIA's required "Neutral," operated from outside the car via the "N" button just ahead of the cockpit.

This must disengage the clutch for a minimum of fifteen minutes.

"Speed limiter—Pit lane" Operates the pit lane speed limiter.
"Engine stop (for start)" Secondary function: the driver must operate this button when the engine is first cranked without either fuel or ignition, in order to build up the pressures. This function only operates when the car is stationary.

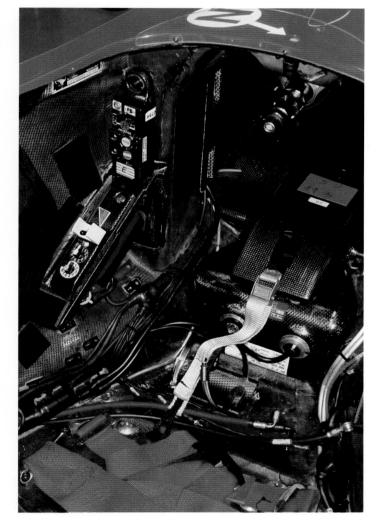

"Under revs"   Lowers the rpm limit for increased durability during a race.

"Radio"   Radio transmit button—only useable when the electrical power is on.

"Spare"   Assignable spare button.

"Mute"   Mutes radio transmissions received.

"Spotello serbatoio"   Manual opening of the refuelling flap, in case of automatic system failure.

"Engine off"   Secondary function: when used in conjunction with button 4, the driver can switch off the engine while keeping all the electronic units powered up, which is required for FIA's software inspection procedure 0.

"Scroll"   Scrolling of the central LCD to display various parameters (see above).

ROTARY SWITCHES

"Brake balance—BB"   Selects brake balance.

"Power steering—PS"   Turns off power steering.

"Active idle—AI—high"   Selection of different drive-by-wire settings for high action in engine braking.

"Mixture—MIX"   Engine mixture setting.

"Active idle—AI—low"   Selection of different drive-by-wire settings for low action in engine braking.

"Recovery—REC"   Recovery from system failure: in every position the driver can switch off electronic functions in case of failure; for example, engine speed sensor; gearbox barrel sensor; clutch position sensor; drive-by-wire; differential pressure sensor; steering wheel sensors.

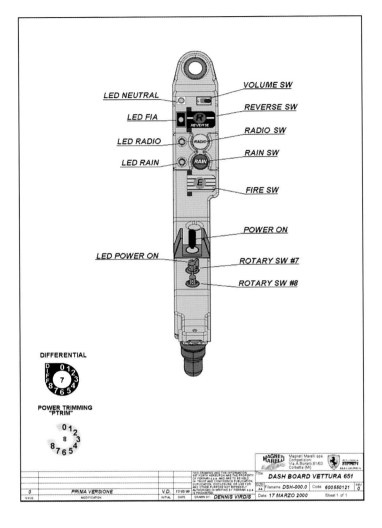

LEFT: *[Fig. 11-10] Additional controls are located on a small panel down by the driver's left thigh. The text describes their functions.*

RIGHT: *[Fig. 11-11] The layout of the electrical/electronic system on a modern Formula 1 car is as much a part of the design process as any other part or system. The majority of the black boxes are grouped around the C of G—in the side pods and cockpit—as they tend to be heavy components.*

The control console on the left of the cockpit has the following functions, from the top (Figures 11-9 and 11-10):

- LED to indicate neutral is selected.
- Radio volume switch—high or low.
- FIA LED—to indicate that the accident data recorder is functioning correctly.
- Reverse switch—to select reverse gear.
- Radio "on" switch and indicator LED—this can be used when electrical power is off.
- Rain light switch and indicator LED.
- Fire extinguisher switch, with guard.

- Power switch and indicator LED.
- Rotary switch 7: Differential settings.
- Rotary switch 8: "Power trimming—PTRIM": engine mapping settings for different torque curve shapes.

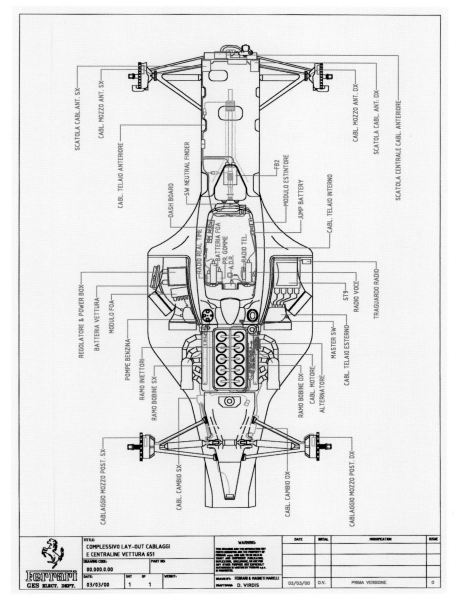

ELECTRICS AND ELECTRONICS.

For years, the prime objective in the design of a racing car electrical system was to ensure that when a wire fractured, the alternator failed, or the battery fell off, the car did not stop running and was capable of finishing the race. Today, the electrical system is as essential a part of the car as the engine and wheels (Figure 11-11). As much effort is put into specifying, designing, building, and testing the system as any other part of the car.

Computer aided design, engineering, simulation, and analysis depends on the quality of the input data. Precise knowledge of the operating condition of each component and system has become the cornerstone of the design process and has resulted in the car becoming a mobile measurement system. Ferrari has the benefit of Magneti Marelli as its electrical and electronics system partner. The F1-2000 has the capability of measuring 250 channels of data at a rate of up to 1KHz per channel, either storing it, telemetering it back to the pits, or using it to control functions on the car. The day is not far off—and indeed may have already arrived—when 1,000 data channels are available to the engineers.

In the early 1990s, when control systems were unregulated, loom complexity and weight started to become a problem. Every sensor and actuator required several copper wires connecting it to one or more central computers, and reliability suffered. Digital network technology came to the rescue, reducing the size of the looms to manageable proportions. Epitomising the problem is the steering wheel, which must be detachable. Until networked systems were available, the maximum number of functions that could be incorporated into the wheel was limited by the number of connector pins that could be fitted into the connector in the middle of the column. With multiplexing, only eight wires and, hence, eight connector pins are required to connect the wheel via its quick-release mechanism to the car, in spite of its multiplicity of switches, buttons, lights, and LCDs.

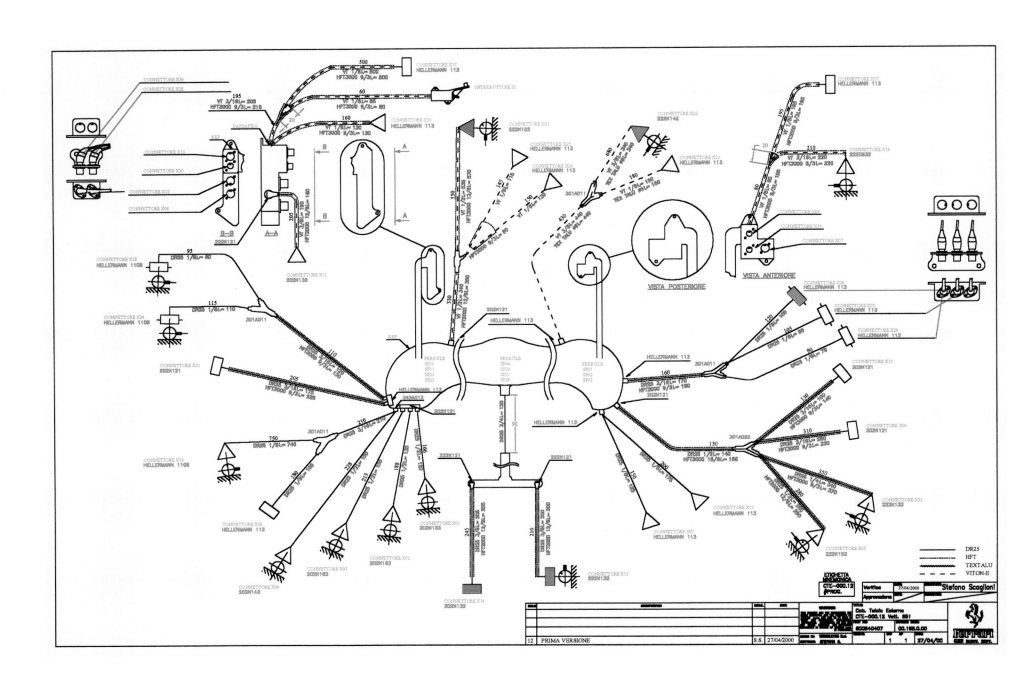

For serviceability, the Ferrari F1-2000's electrical system is split into five zones, with individual looms in each (Figure 11-12).

LEFT: *[Fig. 11-12] The schematic of the main chassis loom shows just how complex electrical and electronic systems on Formula 1 cars have become.*

RIGHT: *[Fig. 11-13] The key engine sensors, many of which affect the control of the engine, are grouped in a replaceable unit that is antivibration mounted to the engine.*

FRONT CHASSIS LOOM:

- Left-hand and right-hand front hub connector units for all hub and brake sensors
- Left-hand, right-hand, and central connector units for miscellaneous sensors and actuators (e.g., power steering)

INTERNAL CHASSIS LOOM:

- Steering wheel
- Steering torque sensor (power steering)
- Control console
- Control unit for power steering and brake balance
- Voice radio
- Fire extinguisher
- FIA accident data recorder
- Burst telemetry transmitter
- Real-time data transmitter
- Tyre pressure sensor unit (telemetry)
- Left-hand, right-hand, and expansion connector units for miscellaneous sensors
- Neutral finder switch and auxiliary battery
- Jump battery connector—external power supply, FIA download, PC connection via Ethernet

EXTERIOR CHASSIS LOOM:

- Lap trigger
- Main control unit
- FOM control unit for FOA TV cameras
- Power box (voltage regulator)
- Battery
- Laser connector (ride-height sensors)
- Left-hand, right-hand, and expansion connector units for miscellaneous sensors

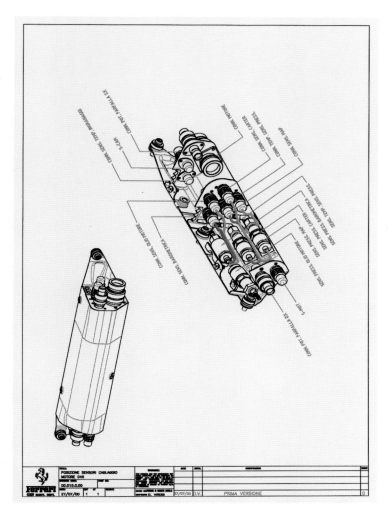

ENGINE LOOM:

- Ignition coils
- Fuel injectors
- Alternator
- Engine sensors (Figure 11-13)

GEARBOX LOOM:

- Left-hand and right-hand rear hub connector units for all hub and brake sensors
- Left-hand and right-hand gearbox sensors and actuators

LEFT: [Fig. 11-14] As many components as can be fit are packed in around the driver, especially electronics boxes, as these are heavy items and need to be as near the C of G as possible.

TOP RIGHT: The Magneti Marelli ECU is mounted under the right side pod, as low as possible. Routing of the wiring loom is part of the design layout of the car, as the loom is a heavy component and a potential source of reliability problems.

BOTTOM RIGHT: [Fig. 11-16] The voltage regulator is mounted under the left side pod, as low as possible and with its finned top surface protruding into the radiator duct. The battery is mounted on the side of the duct, and above the duct is the lap marker receiver.

As far as is possible, the heavy components (e.g., the main control unit, battery, and voltage regulator) are mounted in the centre of the car and as low as possible. The two main chassis looms, which contain many copper wires, are routed under the monocoque to keep their weight low down as well (Figure 11-14). The voltage regulator and the main control unit require cooling, and so they are mounted under the radiator intake ducts on each side with a heat transfer surface, finned for the voltage regulator, sticking through the duct to be cooled by the airstream (Figure 11-16).

The status of all critical systems and components is monitored via telemetry while the car is running. Typically, system temperatures and pressures are measured, while shaft speeds provide data on system states at any moment. During reliability, engine, tyre, aerodynamic, suspension, and performance testing, many more parameters are measured by fitting extra sensors as required. Not all data is sent by telemetry to the pits; much of it is stored in on-board memory for downloading when the car stops. On return to the pit garage, the car is connected to the race and system engineers' computers, and at the same time auxiliary power is connected to maintain the car's systems, as the battery capacity is small. Data is downloaded to a central archive for access by those with suitable authority, including major technical partners, and is transmitted by satellite link back to the factory. Status checking and parameter and software changes then take place before the next run.

FERRARI'S TECHNICAL PARTNER FOR ELECTRICS: MAGNETI MARELLI.

The Fiat-owned Magneti Marelli Companies are international leaders in the design and production of high-tech components and systems for the automotive industry.

Magneti Marelli has taken an active part in the preparation of engines for competitions right from the year after its founding in 1919. Since then it has been involved with car, motorcycle, and powerboat racing, and competition aircraft.

Ferrari has always raced with Magneti Marelli equipment, and now relies on the company for all its electric and electronic development.

12

Safety Systems and Structures

S ince the 1970s, the FIA has progressively raised the safety standards for Formula 1 cars, based on background research carried out by the FIA and a few major automobile manufacturers who are involved in racing. Up until that time, the chance of a racing driver being killed or badly injured was high, but today a Formula 1 driver does not expect to be killed or seriously injured while racing or testing, even though high-speed accidents still inevitably occur. Part of the reduction in risk has come from improvements to the circuits,

LEFT: *Advanced composites have freed the designers from the flat panels prevalent with sheet metal structures. They are now able to combine aerodynamic curves with the structural stiffness and impact performance requirements.*

RIGHT: *A detail of the FEA analysis of the FIA 40KN nose push-off test.*

medical intervention procedures, and the way the races are conducted (in the '60s, the chance of a driver being killed or seriously injured was 1 in 8 accidents, and in some years, 1 in 4; today it is better than 1 in 50). However, the technical regulations now lay down the systems and structures, along with test specifications, that ensure that the driver is protected within a strong safety cell, surrounded by energy-absorbing structures. Inside the cockpit, he is restrained and protected against high decelerations and yet can be accessed for medical intervention, if need be.

The sections of the Formula 1 Technical Regulations that deal with safety are Article 13 (Cockpit), Article 14 (Safety

Equipment), Article 15 (Safety Structures), Article 16 (Impact Testing), Article 17 (Roll Structure Testing), and Article 18 (Static Load Testing). The philosophy behind these regulations is to define the test conditions that must be met and to allow the designers to find the lightest and best way of meeting them, rather than specifying a construction that must be adhered to. The FIA has had to continuously monitor how the constructors go about meeting the regulations to ensure that their designs not only pass the actual tests but also provide a broad spectrum of protection for a variety of impact scenarios. More time and effort by all parties involved have gone into the development of these regulations than any

other part. The work by the Formula 1 Technical Working Group on safety has now filtered down to the lower formulae, to the benefit of everyone who races.

Road car manufacturers, who may have hundreds of thousands of any particular model used over millions of kilometres on the roads, gain the benefit of a large database of different accident scenarios and how their products perform in reality under a variety of impact conditions. With just a handful of a particular design, running for little more than 50,000km during their useful life, Formula 1 constructors will be unlucky to have more than five serious impacts among all of them in a year to study how their car performs in an impact that will inevitably be different from the ones they have investigated for the FIA impact tests. At Silverstone in 1999, Michael Schumacher's Ferrari suffered a major frontal impact after it lost its rear brakes at Stowe corner, hitting the tyre barrier at around 107kph. The impact-absorbing nose performed as designed, but, once used up, the car still had a speed of around 80kph. Due to a front wheel swinging back and hitting the side of the monocoque, the monocoque fractured, resulting in Schumacher's leg being broken. He probably lost the Drivers' World Championship as a consequence. If the monocoque had not failed, the sudden deceleration forces involved in the car stopping in a very short distance would have been likely to cause even more severe injuries. The accident gave Ferrari engineers the opportunity to study how their design performed right at the limits of survivable impact severity. The lessons learned have been embodied in the detail design and construction of the F1-2000 and subsequent cars. Proof of this occurred when Schumacher had another high-energy frontal impact while testing at Monza in 2001 without any failure of the monocoque.

The principles behind the safety regulations are to provide the driver with a rigid, strong survival cell, into which he is strapped and restrained such that he does not move into

contact with anything hard when subjected to acceleration forces in an impact from any direction. Surrounding this cell are mounted sacrificial, crushable, energy-absorbing structures, which, upon impact, collapse in a way that limits the maximum deceleration to which the survival cell and, through the restraint system, the driver are both subjected. These crushable structures (the nose of the car, the cone mounted on the rear of the gearbox, to which the rear

LEFT: *The wheel tether inboard anchor points can be seen above the wishbone pivots and the sleeved Zylon tethers leading into the CFRP wishbone leg. Above them are the front electrical connector box and the power steering. The two white reservoirs are for brake fluid.*

RIGHT: *The CFRP nose cone, weighing less than 4kg, absorbs the energy of a 14 metre/sec impact of the car, ballasted to 780 kg, without exceeding a survivable 40g deceleration.*

wing is also mounted, and the side pods) are impact-tested according to the regulations. The structural engineers must give the crushable structures energy-absorbing characteristics such that the energy of the test impact is fully absorbed without exceeding loads that generate excessive peak and average decelerations, all with the lowest possible weight.

The tools structural composite engineers now have at their disposal enable them to optimise the lay-ups of the various elements. FEA (finite element analysis) of composites, allied with precise material strength properties, allows areas subjected to peak stresses to be reinforced locally. Composites have freed designers to create structures with complex double-curvature shapes, which would be very difficult to analyse structurally without FEA. Composites exhibit properties with different characteristics in every direction, especially in shear (these non-isotropic properties are, of course, the whole point of composites, allowing strength to be incorporated only in the directions where required), which also makes analysis more difficult. The dynamic analysis of composite structures was still not fully

LEFT: *FEA analysis of the FIA frontal impact test. The red elements are the most highly stressed, the blue the least. Note the high level of stress in the top edges of the cockpit, which are trying to buckle.*

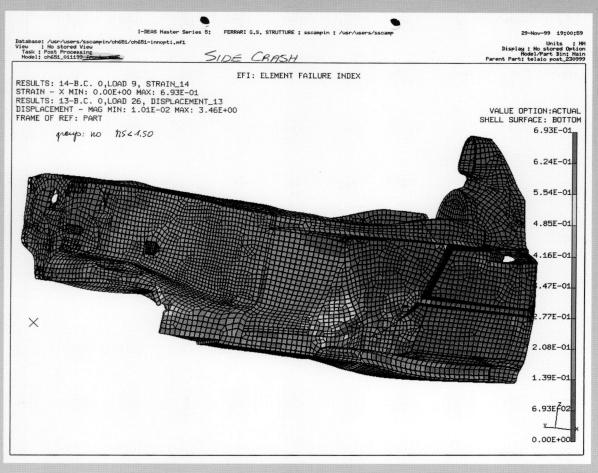

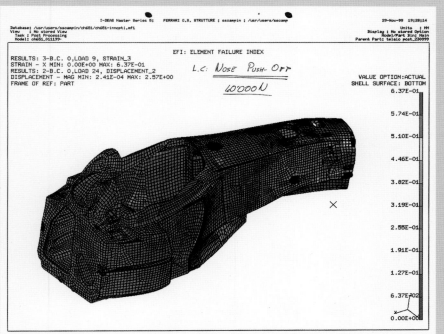

ABOVE: *FEA analysis of the FIA side impact test. The red elements are the most highly stressed, the blue the least.*

LEFT: *FEA analysis of the FIA 40KN nose push-off test, to check the strength of the nose cone fasteners. The red elements are the most highly stressed, the blue the least.*

developed and validated in 2000, but it was able to make a contribution to the design of the F1-2000. By the time the monocoque is designed to withstand the impact and steady state loads during the tests demanded by the regulations, it is generally stiff enough also to do the job required of it as a chassis: connecting the front and rear suspensions and providing a rigid platform to carry the driver, engine, transmission, and fuel, along with the many other smaller and lighter components.

The head and neck of the driver are particularly vulnerable; when subjected to a 40g impact, the roughly 6.5kg head and 1.5kg helmet weigh around 320kg at this acceleration level. The neck is not designed for these loads and will become over-extended if the head does not strike something in the cockpit before it does so. Ensuring that head and brain decelerations do not exceed biomechanical criteria has led to collapsible steering columns and 75mm of Confor foam around the sides and rear of the top of the cockpit surround.

Confor foam exhibits visco-elastic properties such that the harder it is hit, the stiffer it becomes. The development of the HANS device, due to become mandatory in Formula 1 in 2003, sets out to provide a restraint system for the head in a frontal impact.

The high noses of modern Formula 1 cars, developed for aerodynamic reasons, have brought a new danger when one car T-bones another, creating a stiletto-like weapon to penetrate the side of the struck car's monocoque. The FIA initiated an R&D programme to reinforce the sides on the monocoque, and the first results of that programme were incorporated into the Ferrari F1-2000 as 3.5mm thick Kevlar panels along the full sides of the survival cell. Intensive work by the teams and the FIA has allowed these structures to be made in CFRP and to be subjected to test conditions, rather than an actual specified structure, in subsequent years since 2000. Now the side panels are stronger than the crushable nose cone, which is able to absorb as

BELOW: The before and after photographs of the FIA frontal test show how the nose cone is totally destroyed in absorbing the energy in the test.

RIGHT: The results of the frontal impact test are plotted as deceleration, velocity, and displacement. The deceleration is around 15g for most of the nose crush and only rises to 25g as the nose becomes fully crushed after 0.85 metres—all well within the average 40g required by the regulations.

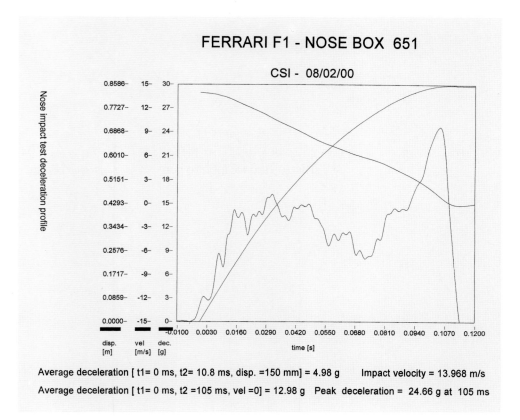

FERRARI F1 - NOSE BOX 651

CSI - 08/02/00

Nose impact test deceleration profile

Average deceleration [t1= 0 ms, t2= 10.8 ms, disp. =150 mm] = 4.98 g   Impact velocity = 13.968 m/s

Average deceleration [t1= 0 ms, t2 =105 ms, vel =0] = 12.98 g   Peak deceleration = 24.66 g at 105 ms

much energy as possible without penetrating the other car's monocoque/safety cell.

If the driver is injured, or even suspected of being injured during an accident, the medical resuscitation crew can extract him without subjecting his potentially injured back and neck to undesirable movement. All the cars must be fitted with a seat that can be removed with the driver strapped into it and a KED (Kendrick extrication device) head and neck support fitted to it. The attachment of these seats has been standardised so that rescue crews around the world can be trained in their removal.

A number of safety regulations relating to the design and build of safety-critical components are included. Perhaps the most important of these is the one dealing with wheel tethering. The wheel, upright, and brake of a Formula 1 car can weigh around 20kg and can have a lot of energy, both linear and rotational, when detached from a car in an accident. It is virtually impossible to guarantee that they will not become detached, especially on an open-wheel car. To provide tethers and their attachments that would not fail when the wheel hit something would require strength such that the car could be arrested when the wheel was stopped by whatever it hit. In 2000, a tether with a breaking load of 50KN was fitted to each wheel. Since that year, the tethers have been doubled, their strength increased, and an R&D programme is under way to build in energy absorption to the tethering system.

Facilitating the R&D behind these safety initiatives is an accident database of the performance of the cars and circuit safety features during accidents, built upon the data gathered by the accident data recorder (ADR) fitted to all Formula 1 cars since 1997. Not only does the ADR log data for the impact itself, but it also records the events leading up to the driver's loss of control and what happens to the car between this point and the impact. The quest for improved safety is continuous. The process by which the FIA stipulates the conditions that must be met by the cars, leaving the teams free to devise individual solutions, is contributing to the evolution of motorsport safety across all classes of racing.

13

Vehicle Dynamics and Simulation

There is one department that does not output tangible hardware and produces no components that go racing on the cars. And yet, both Ross Brawn and Rory Byrne were at great pains to emphasise its contribution to Ferrari's success in the past few years. When Brawn arrived at Maranello, he was disappointed to find that there was little being derived from Ferrari's partnership with parent company Fiat. There was an agreement for Fiat Research Centre (CRF) to undertake projects for Ferrari, but Ferrari was not using it effectively. Problems

LEFT: *Brazilian Grand Prix, Interlagos. Michael Schumacher first, Rubens Barrichello retired. Schumacher took an apparently easy victory, but only after Hakkinen retired. Poor Barrichello seems to be jinxed at his home Grand Prix.*

RIGHT: *This detail of Tony Matthews's working drawing for the car cutaway shows the densely packaged area of the pedals and steering system, through which the driver controls the car.*

were being sent to Turin for CRF to research solutions, but they were not involved enough in the problem and the surrounding circumstances to be able to come up with much in the way of solutions. Brawn changed this, and now CRF works closely with the Scuderia under a research partnership agreement that has Fiat engineers on secondment, working alongside Ferrari engineers to identify problem areas and, where needed, to call on specialists in CRF.

One CRF engineer, who was working as a race engineer on gear-change control systems when Brawn arrived, was Marco Fainello. Brawn spotted his potential, and he now leads the Vehicle Dynamics Department, reporting to Rory Byrne.

"Originally there was a collaboration between Ferrari and

CRF for ten years, which had brought little benefit to Ferrari," Fainello recalls. "Ferrari used to send CRF the problems it did not have time to deal with, but they [CRF] could not understand what the real problem was because no one had time to explain it properly and they did not have the data. The Formula 1 culture, time scales, and way of doing things is quite different from the normal car business. So, we selected a few people, the best of course, and they stay at Ferrari for a few weeks or months to understand the problems and to look for the opportunities—which may be something other than that we are asking them about, some problem we don't realise we have. We are now a group that comprises some CRF and some Ferrari engineers, sometimes they are

BOTTOM RIGHT: *The essential data for measuring the dynamic response of a racing car is speed and lateral and longitudinal accelerations. The data is either telemetered to the pits or stored on board for download on return to the pits. The data can be either plotted against time or distance around the lap, as shown here. Schumacher's 1:26.16 qualifying lap of Silverstone was only good enough for fifth place on the grid*

TOP RIGHT: *Silverstone circuit diagram.*

working here, sometimes in Turin. Now we influence the design of the suspension and layout of the car, which was not true before."

Vehicle dynamics is the understanding and the description in mathematical terms of the motion of a vehicle. As applied to a racing car, the simulation of its dynamics using powerful computers and specialist software has helped engineers predict performance and scientifically create repeatable results in a way that had not been possible before. Ferrari is probably at the forefront of this technology and is now using it to influence the design direction of the car in ways that are not always obvious without these tools. The limitations to

just how much vehicle dynamic simulation can predict outright performance and the control and stability of a Formula 1 car depends on the sophistication and validation of certain key components, particularly the driver, the tyre, and the dampers.

Starting almost from scratch, Fainello established organised archives of the data and procedures for the testing of components, from springs to the wind tunnels, and to check the output of simulations against track data. He also developed methodology to integrate the track data into the simulations themselves, so that comparisons could be made at different levels.

"We get data from Bridgestone, in the form of coefficients derived from flat-bed tyre test machines," Fainello says. "We add certain corrections and data on pressure sensitivity and vertical stiffness, and damping characteristics. However, the data is not enough to make proper simulations, only to determine some trends—it is our biggest problem. There is a big job of correlating the rig data with the track data. We have to get good measurements from the track, and then we can use the car as a test rig for actual race tyres on the actual track and use the data to correct the rig coefficients."

One test of how good the simulations are is whether they can be used to determine the set-up of the cars before they go to a race. Explains Fainello: "Before each race we are proposing a reference set-up, sometimes two, and the race engineers have these set-ups and they use them however they want. We then keep track of what they do, how they

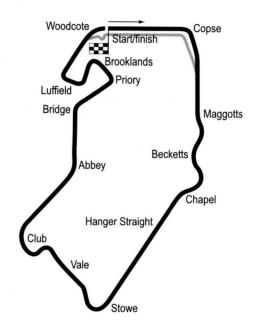

evolve the car, so that we can understand what is going on. After a few years when it was difficult to get the confidence in simulations, when the race engineers used their experience and we sometimes got it wrong, they now use the reference set-up quite a lot, especially as there is so little time at a race. As the year goes on, we improve our level of simulation, and they get more confident in it.

"One limitation to how good the simulation can be is the driver model, and we do not have a good driver model. It is almost a bigger problem than the tyres. We know that in theory we could have a set-up that is much, much faster that what we are using, but that the driver would not be able to drive it."

The driver, as a control system (sometimes referred to as the "emotional control system") must be included in simulations if the ultimate performance of the man-machine combination is to be explored. It has been established for many years that unstable aircraft are more responsive than

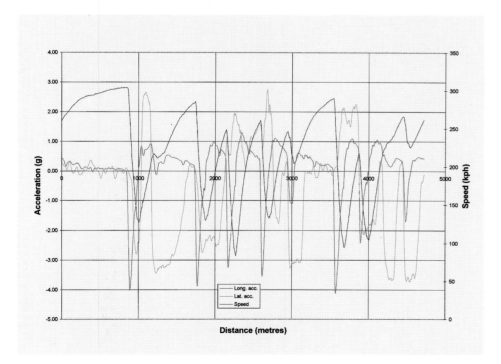

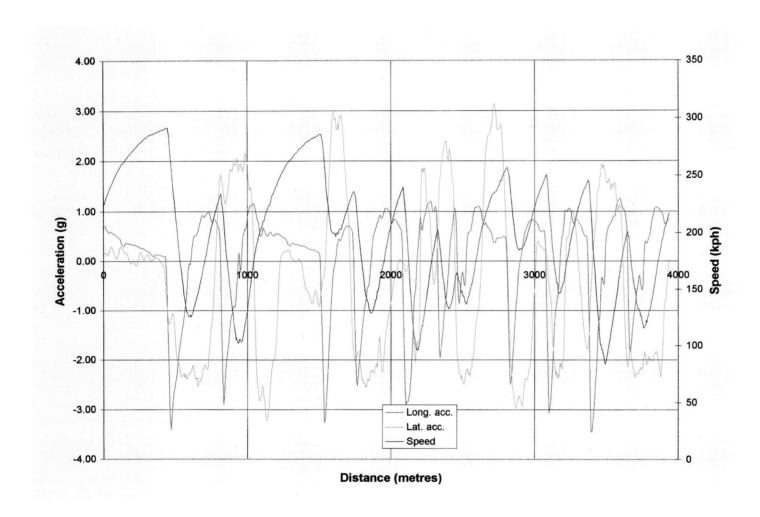

stable ones, but that it requires a computer to fly them with the pilot merely demanding a response, while the computer makes the actual control inputs *and corrections.* The same is true in a car, but the computer and software needed are in the realm of driver aids, which the FIA is determined to ban. Thus, how far towards an unstable and, hence, more responsive car the engineers can go depends upon a full understanding of the physical and psychological limitations of the driver and the engineers' ability to model him in simulations.

Ferrari is exploring a number of approaches to this issue, but Fainello confirms that they have not yet found one that they are entirely happy with. One approach is to simulate all the inputs a driver receives, such as accelerations detected by the semi-circular canals in his ears, forces experienced on his body, particularly through his hands on the steering

wheel, and optical and retinal flows, which are the way we detect and analyse steady motions, such as speed and yaw rotation. Measuring these biological sensor inputs is by no means easy, and even when they're simulated, it is then necessary to decide which of them he takes notice of (attention), how quickly he processes them (cognitive performance), what he decides to do (neural processing), and how quickly and accurately he can do it (muscle response).

Another approach in the simulation is to analyse and reproduce typical responses to typical situations. For example, if the car hits a bump while accelerating out of a corner and the rear wheels break traction and the car oversteers, what are the driver reactions to the throttle and steering?

Fainello believes that none of these approaches will be completely successful and that the search continues for another way forward.

It is now fairly common practice in motorsport to develop and set up the damping of the car on a four-post or

seven-post road simulation rig. Most Formula 1 teams have one, and there are many available for hiring time on. It was therefore somewhat surprising to discover that Ferrari does not have one in the racing team, though it does have access to one in the road car R&D department. Nor does the company feel able to rely on such a rig to develop damping, preferring to use simulation. Fainello explains: "There are two classes of problem: firstly to know what is the best damping, because it is difficult to simulate on a bench, and the other is to know exactly what a tyre is doing. We asked Bridgestone for some special measurements, and they have produced some good results for stiffness and damping at different speeds and frequencies—it is not really damping, as the tyre is made of rubber, so it is also hysteresis—and we are using these in our model."

Fainello believes there are several limitations in the seven-post rigs that discourage Ferrari from using one to actually reproduce what is happening on the track for damper development. The fact that the tyre is not rotating is one, and the lack of a real person in the car is another—dummies do not respond correctly to the range of frequencies they are most interested in, and yet represents 15 percent of the mass of the car. Additionally, the rig is a complex structure, excited by high-performance electro-hydraulic actuators. The response of the whole, rig and car, is measured, and the two must be separated to understand the car alone. It is all too easy for something to change during a run—temperature, for example, which inevitably rises during the course of a test as energy is absorbed by the system—and to spend the session chasing stable results.

Fainello comments, "Instead we simulated the seven-post rig and a non-rotating tyre, and validated the simulation on the rig, getting the same results up to a certain frequency—we are most interested in frequencies up to 20Hz and monitor above that, though we do not yet see any great effects. We

then used the simulation to minimise load variation at the tyre contact patch, which is one of the goals of damping."

Fainello's department developed its simulation to the point where it linked it to an optimisation routine and tasked it with coming up with "ideal" damper settings. The results were damper settings that were significantly different to anything the department had tried before.

"We tested them on the track, and the drivers were very happy with the feel, and the car was slightly quicker, though not by a lot," Fainello says. "We then realised we knew nothing about damping, and we tried to use the result to understand the problem better. It forced us to look harder at the car as a whole, rather than as four individual corners, and to include the aerodynamics. It becomes much more complex than you can normally consider in your mind."

If ever there was the equivalent of an "Alan Turing Test of Artificial Intelligence" for vehicle dynamics simulation, it is arriving at damper settings that are in a different ball-

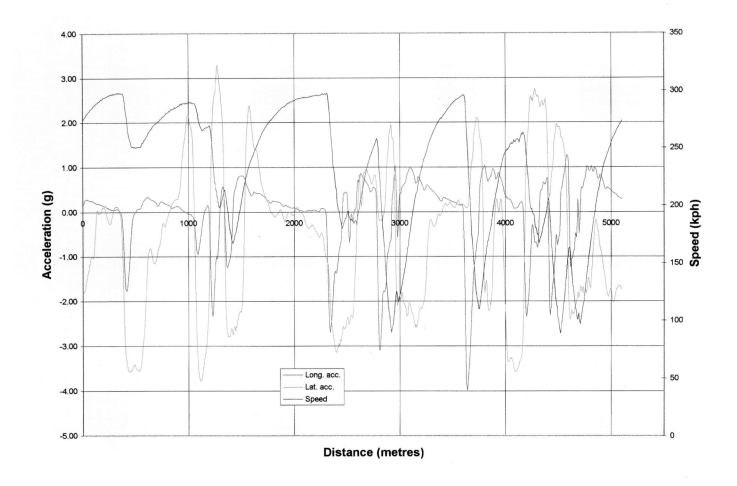

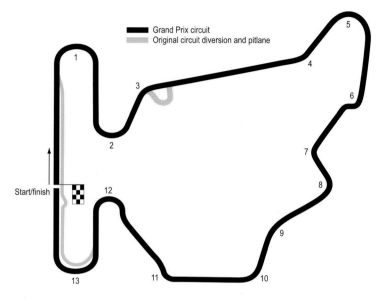

Grand Prix circuit
Original circuit diversion and pitlane

Start/finish

park from those normally arrived at by rig or track testing and yet that actually improve the performance of the car.

In 2000, one of the few means by which the control engineers could influence the vehicle dynamics was the differential, and even then it was only in a limited way. The only inputs to the control law were engine torque (measured or derived), the difference in rear wheel speeds, and the difference in rear wheel torques. Simulation was essential for the development of suitable algorithms and understanding the response of the car as influenced by the differential.

"We tried to distinguish between the classical different situations like braking, turn-in, mid-corner and accelerating out of the corner, and we have a routine that tries to establish which state the car is in at any moment. That was actually the most difficult thing to do because we were limited on the sensors we could use by the rather ambiguously worded regulation," Fainello says.

The main problem teams faced was to determine where on the track the car was at any moment (i.e., which corner) and, thus, which setting was required. The use of car speed, or its integral to determine position around a lap, was not per-

mitted. However, software engineers could use measured or calculated engine torque, the latter using engine speed and throttle opening. When they then tried to determine, from engine speed and throttle, where on the circuit the car was at any moment, they ran into inevitable problems.

Fainello continues: "It was quite difficult to have an algorithm to distinguish very reliably the different situation on the corner, without continuously jumping from one to the other; we had to build in hysteresis and those sort of things. The other big problem we had was to achieve a smooth transition from one state to another, so in the end it turned out to be a state control. We did more, but this was the basic control. We looked at what we wanted to do in an ideal world, and then saw how little we could give up to cope with the rules.

"In braking, you have a problem of stability, and locking the differential gives better stability in nearly all conditions. Turn-in and mid-corner, you have to find an ideal between stability and understeer, somewhere intermediate and hence more complex. The tuning for that one was much related to the car set-up and to the driver. Some drivers preferred different amounts of locking; they could choose, but in 2000 could adjust the differential only when the car was stationary at a pit stop. Under acceleration there is a common misunderstanding that a locked differential gives understeer, which is not always true. It was the most difficult thing to tune because it was necessary to have enough stability, not too much oversteer, and enough traction capability. It was a combination of experiment and simulation, but very much sensitive to the tyre data accuracy—it required very detailed data—and of course changed as the tyres and track changed. For instance, we are working with Bridgestone on tyre temperature sensitivity, based on rig and track measurements. Experience counts for a lot in this area.

"It became clear early on with this work that there is not

much advantage that you can get from the control of the differential itself. The advantage you can get is that the differential control allows you to use different set-ups, and then you develop the advantage because you can make the driver accept a more aggressive set-up. We did the back-to-back comparison many times—a standard differential, or an active one set to be on a fixed setting—and tested it against a fully active one, and there is not much difference. The fact that the differential allows you to use a different set-up approach, different suspension, different weight distribution, allows you to get the best advantage. Of course it is trickier making a car that is less stable, maybe too unstable for the driver to cope with, and stabilise it, make it driveable with the differential. Of course it brought a lot of problems in managing the tool because there is not a differential expert that makes the best set-up; it must be under the control of the race engineer because it is a general process. But, the race engineer does not have enough time or enough control experience to develop the differential, and so you need to organise the job at the track in a certain way. Sometimes at races we had to go right back to basics or we were in danger of getting lost in the complexity.

"Another aspect of setting up the differential is that with other tools you rely a lot on the driver adjustment and feedback, so normally they set the general direction as they know whether something is better. With the differential, my feeling is that the driver is not so helpful, as he could not distinguish a direction as it has a very non-linear behaviour."

Because the differential is such a powerful means of influencing the stability of the car, it steps in and may produce a result to a change that is illogical within the race engineers' normal experience, based on the drivers' comments. Ferrari found a better approach to differential development by not telling the driver what changes had been made and just asking him to drive the car, without trying to work out what was happening.

Fainello says: "Active differentials are something very strange and do not behave logically like downforce, which the driver understands from his experience. The differential steers the car. Sometimes with a locked differential he feels he has a lot of traction because he can put his foot on the accelerator with less oversteer reaction from the car, but the acceleration is less by an amount he cannot feel; the data shows it to be less.

"That is the situation. Simulation helps a lot, but you have to do a lot of testing, and we did a lot at Fiorano, which is very good for this sort of work. When we realised that the differential was more complex than other systems, we followed the work very closely, but by 2000 we had got on top of it and the situation stabilised. After that the modifications came from the normal test and race development process."

With one of the pacing factors of vehicle dynamics and simulation being the tyres, Fainello's department is continually looking for technologies to enable it to better measure what the tyres are doing. Access to what is happening at the contact patch is difficult, and techniques and sensors to measure load, slip angle, and temperature at the contact patch are on-going research projects. Ferrari's increasingly close relationship with Bridgestone is bound to yield major benefits in the future.

When Ross Brawn described the new Ferraris at their launches in 1997, 1998, and 1999, there was a note of caution in what he said with reference to expectations for the cars each year. In 2000, that caution had gone and he was distinctly bullish about Ferrari's prospects. Those predictions were not just based on either his mood at the time nor the need to handle press speculation about the cars. He knew what the cars were capable of and had a pretty good idea where they would be relative to McLaren. The knowledge to back up his predictions, which in each case turned out to be accurate, was based in part on the simulation work of the Vehicle Dynamics Department.

FERRARI'S TECHNICAL PARTNER FOR VEHICLE DYNAMICS: FIAT.

Ferrari's parent company, Fiat, has been in the automobile business since 1899 and started racing internationally in its earliest days, winning its first race in 1904. The company is the industrial giant of Italy, operating in the aerospace, construction, industrial, marine, electrical, agricultural, and automobile sectors. Today it is a global corporation, turning over more than €58 billion annually.

While the resources and expertise of this multi-faceted organisation are available to Ferrari, its main point of contact is Fiat Research Centre, set up in 1976 to bring together and disseminate the research activities of all parts of Fiat. CRF employs more than 1,000 people, half of whom are graduates, and is located just outside Turin, the birthplace of Fiat.

CRF brings to Ferrari specialist knowledge and expertise in measurement, analysis, testing, and materials. The majority of joint programmes are long-term research, such as the development of vehicle dynamics simulations.

14

Performance

RIGHT: *[Fig. 14-2] The g-g-V diagram illustrates the performance envelope of a racing car with aerodynamic downforce, under a given set of conditions. The sides form the limiting combinations of longitudinal and lateral acceleration that the car is able to generate, and the height is the maximum speed. A driver may not be able to access all the edges of the envelope due to stability and/or control limitations. How much he can access is a function of the car set-up and his skill and bravery.*

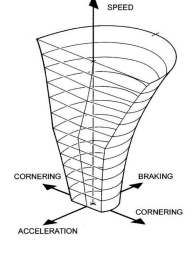

The record books list the performance of Formula 1 cars solely as their average speeds around a given circuit, both as a speed for a single lap in qualifying and as an average over the race distance. Road car assessments, as reported by the motoring press, measure and report a number of other parameters in an attempt to compare the performance of a variety of cars in a particular class. These include acceleration (0 to 100kph, standing quarter-mile, acceleration times in the gears, etc.), deceleration (100 to 0kph), top speed, maximum lateral acceleration, and

various manoeuvres that set out to assess the handling characteristics. The performance of any car is much more complex than any of these references, but in the case of a racing car, we are able to pare it down to those characteristics that contribute directly to its racing abilities. Compromises between ride and handling and such issues as legal speed limits do not come into the analysis. In my book *Formula 1 Technology*, I attempt to define the performance envelope of a Formula 1 car, or indeed any racing car, by means of a diagram known as the g-g-V diagram. The g-g diagram is pretty well known in automotive testing (Ref: 14.2), and illustrates the limits of all combinations of longitudinal acceleration,

both accelerating and braking, and lateral acceleration; the car is able to manoeuvre at any point within the diagram. This works well to show the performance envelope for a car that does not have aerodynamic downforce. Downforce increases the size of the g-g diagram as speed increases, and so, by adding a third axis for speed, a 3-D performance envelope is produced, the surface of which represents the limits of performance of the vehicle (Figure 14-2).

The g-g-V diagram only represents the performance envelope under one set of circumstances. The size and shape of the diagram are a function of many parameters, some of which change continuously (e.g., tyre temperature, track

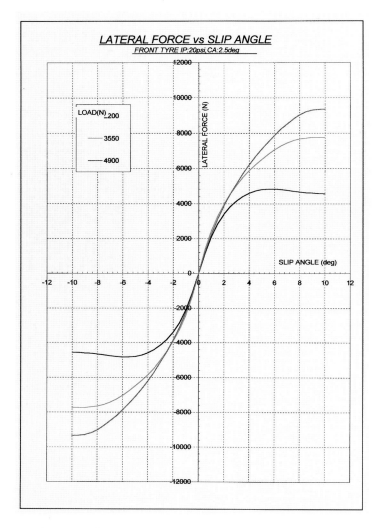

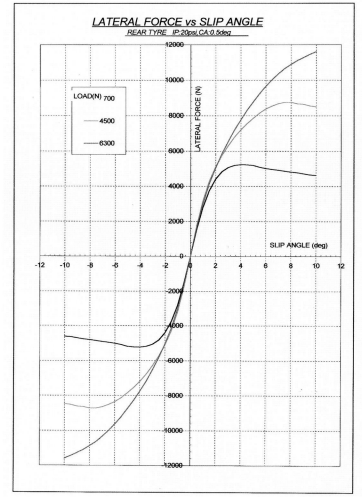

The front and rear tyre cornering characteristics were measured on a flat-bed tyre test rig and show the cornering forces generated as the slip angle changes for three different vertical loads. Note that the peak slip angles are 5 degrees (F) and 4 degrees (R) at the lowest load, but rise to more than 10 degrees at the highest loads.

RIGHT: *[Fig. 14-5 and 14-6]*

Front and rear tyre combined longitudinal and lateral force characteristics. These tyre ellipses show how the traction and braking capabilities of the tyres are affected by combined cornering with traction or braking.

surface, track elevation and camber, brake temperature, ambient temperature, wind, and of course, the set-up of the car). Suspension and wing settings have a major influence,and are used to achieve different compromises for different circuits to optimise the average performance at all points on the track.

A performance envelope is a surface that represents the limits of performance at which the vehicle is able to operate, and it makes no concessions as to how easy it is to operate at the limits, i.e., whether it is within the capability of a human operator. The size of the envelope is determined by the car parameters that contribute to the simple Newtonian equation: Acceleration = Force/Mass, that is, the weight, power, aerodynamic downforce, drag, brakes, and the tyres, by which means the majority of the forces are generated. The ability of the human driver to operate at or near the surface of the envelope depends on all the other car parameters: weight distribution, moments of inertia, yaw damping,

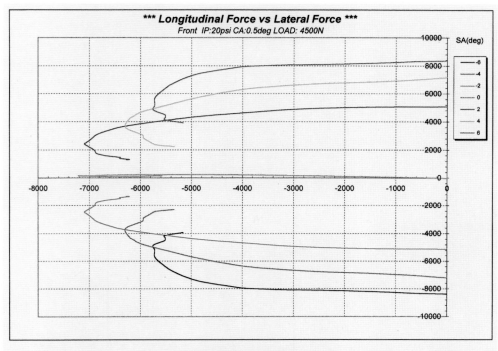

*** Longitudinal Force vs Lateral Force ***
Front IP:20psi CA:0.5deg LOAD: 4500N

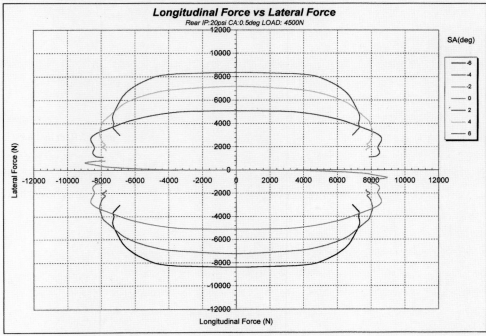

Longitudinal Force vs Lateral Force
Rear IP:20psi CA:0.5deg LOAD: 4500N

tyre characteristics at their limits, centre of gravity height, transient aerodynamic characteristics, suspension kinematics, spring and damper settings, engine driveability, differential characteristics, etc. These characteristics can be summarised as contributing to stability and control, where stability is the ability of a vehicle to return to its state of equilibrium when disturbed and control is the ability of the operator to move from one equilibrium state to another.

It is inevitable that engineers have tried to overcome the human operating limits by using computers to alter artificially the stability and control characteristics inherent in the particular combination of mechanical components of the car. The technology was developed for fly-by-wire aircraft and started to enter road cars in the 1980s. The peak of this technology's application to Formula 1 was 1993, when active suspension, power-assisted ABS brakes, traction control, rear steer, and active differentials all made appearances, after which the FIA attempted to ban all driver aids. In 2000, only a limited range of ways of controlling the gearbox and clutch, the differential, and the drive-by-wire throttles were permitted; all other driver aids were banned. Due to problems of definition and after scrutinising the software that controlled other aspects of the car, it was decided in 2002 that engine and transmission control should be free, allowing traction control and unlimited differential control (other than torque-steer, which was specifically not permitted), everything else being banned.

Establishing the size and shape of the g-g-V diagram requires a certain level of knowledge of the mass layout of the car; the aerodynamic maps (i.e., the sensitivity to front and rear ride heights of the downforce, its distribution, and the drag) for the various combinations of wing settings; tyre load and camber characteristics for lateral and longitudinal force generation, particularly when combined; and the springing characteristics of the suspension and tyres, in order to

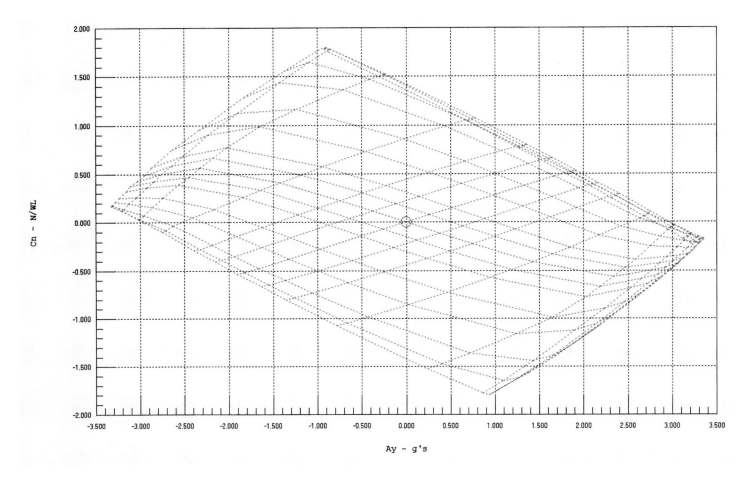

LEFT: [Fig. 14-7] The moment diagram plots Yawing moment coefficient (Cn) against Lateral acceleration (Ay) for a single condition, in this case: 180kph and 0.6g longitudinal acceleration. The lines running up, from left to right, are lines of constant vehicle slip angle; the lines running down, left to right, are lines of constant steer angle. The limits of the diagram are the manoeuvring limits of the car for this condition. The car has zero Cn (i.e., the driver is unable to control the car anymore with steering input) at a lateral acceleration of 2.9g, but it will generate up to 3.3g while understeering at the limit.

determine the car attitude under aerodynamic and inertia loads. The power available and the maximum braking force possible impose additional limits.

Establishing how much of the envelope can be accessed by the driver, (i.e., the stability and control characteristics and how the driver uses his driving skills to cope with them) requires a level of analysis and input data that is only available to the engineers working directly on the design and development of the car. However, by comparing actual data measured on the car while it's driven at or near its limits, with a g-g-V diagram based on available data, it is possible to identify how much of the performance envelope the driver is able or wishes to use and which parts of it he avoids. It may

then be possible to use the output from the model that calculates the g-g-V diagram to look into and try and understand the reasons for this. In this way, we can establish both the maximum potential performance of the car and why only a part of that performance is useable on the track.

Ferrari supplied the author with sufficient data for the F1-2000's characteristics to develop a basic quasi-static model, thus enabling an estimate of the car's performance envelope to be made. Ferrari also supplied data for a number of Michael Schumacher's qualifying laps in 2000. With this data, it is possible both to explore the car's potential and to gain some insight into how much of it Schumacher was able to exploit.

DATA

Ferrari supplied the following data:

- Typical power and torque curves for the Tipo 049 engine—see chapter 5
- Mass distribution data, as listed in the car specification in chapter 4
- Typical aero. maps for front and rear ride heights and wing set-ups for various lift/drag compromises—see chapter 7
- The range of suspension stiffness used—see car specification in chapter 4
- Speed, rpm, and lateral and longitudinal acceleration traces for Schumacher's qualifying laps on a number of circuits.
- Bridgestone supplied curves for typical tyre characteristics. As noted previously, this data is measured on a tyre test rig and suffers from poor simulation of the tyre track interface. Ferrari supplied correction factors, based on track measurements.

ENGINE.

The engine performance has a limited effect on the performance envelope of a Formula 1 car. The maximum power determines the top speed, but the torque curve only comes into play once the car is no longer traction limited—above about 150kph—determining acceleration.

GEARBOX.

Gear changing was manually commanded in 2000, with the control of engine, clutch, and change mechanism being under computer control once the command was accepted. Non-acceptance of the command is possible if a down-change is requested that would result in the engine over-revving, in which case the driver must re-initiate the down-change. Up-changes are made without the use of the clutch and solely involve a cut in the ignition to slow the engine. Power-off times are around 0.03 to 0.04 seconds, during which the car decelerates due to drag at more than 1.0g at speeds greater than 250kph. When the new gear engages, the engine rpm will have only fallen by around half the required 2,000 rpm or so needed for the higher gear. The shock load on the drivetrain generates variations in the acceleration of the car to the order of +/-0.5g. Down-changes, where speed of change is not critical, may employ the clutch to smooth the re-engagement, avoiding the shock loads that disturb the rear tyres and destabilise the car under braking.

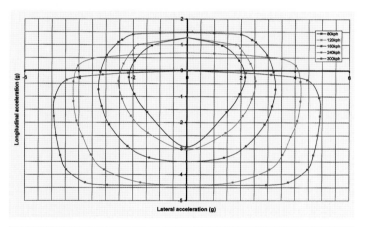

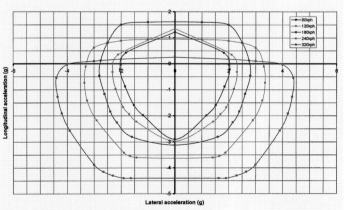

BRAKES.

The maximum braking deceleration is either governed by the brake pressure that the driver is capable of generating with his foot, which tends to be the limiting factor at high speeds, or the maximum tyre grip. When he initially applies the brakes, the discs and pads may not be at optimum temperature, and it may take a short time to generate maximum retardation. The initial application will be open loop i.e., the driver applies the brakes with a pre-determined foot pressure and does not expect to have to immediately correct

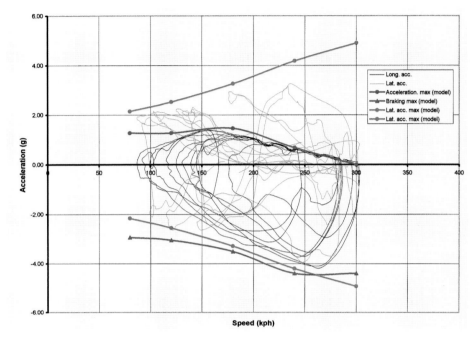

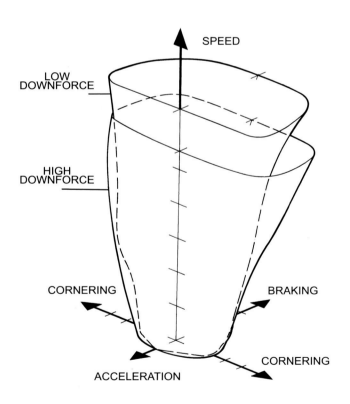

that application, and it is therefore beneficial if the driver cannot lock the wheels with the initial push on the brake pedal. As the speed drops and the downforce reduces, he will have to modulate the brake pressure to prevent the wheels locking. It is most likely that the brake balance will be set such that the front wheels lock first, as this is the stable configuration at the limit.

The braking limits imposed on the performance envelope in this analysis are derived from the track data from a number of circuits, as the mechanical data is not available.

MASS.

The mass of the vehicle and the longitudinal and vertical centre of gravity positions are all that are needed for a quasi-static analysis. It is important to separate sprung and unsprung masses, as only the sprung mass moves under aerodynamic and inertia loads, affecting C of G height. Roll, pitch, and yaw inertias are not needed until the responses to control inputs

LEFT: *[Fig. 14-10] g-g-V diagrams for the Ferrari F1-2000, in high and low-downforce set-ups. The range of performance envelopes that can be set up on the car is graphically illustrated. (Tony Matthews)*

and disturbances are analysed.

The mass of a Formula 1 car depends on the amount of fuel being carried, which also affects weight distribution and C of G height. As previously mentioned, Formula 1 cars are often built with a weight less than the mandatory minimum of 600kg, including driver. Consequently, 70kg or so of ballast is distributed as low as possible in the car to lower the C of G and to permit variations of weight distribution according to the set-up for a particular circuit.

The analysis has been made on the F1-2000 in qualifying trim, as this is the set-up used when the track data that Ferrari supplied was measured. The actual values of weight distribution depend on the exact aerodynamic set-up and tyre balance, details of which go beyond the scope of this analysis, based on the limited data sets supplied.

AERODYNAMICS.

It used to be sufficient to measure the front and rear axle downforce and the drag in the wind tunnel, but with the increasing contribution to the downforce from the lower surfaces of the car, in ground effect, the height above the ground and the pitch attitude became extremely important. Aerodynamicists started to measure characteristics throughout the range of axle ride heights, and the aerodynamic coefficients are now plotted as aero. maps of CLf, CLr, CD, and balance against front and rear axle ride heights. Representative maps for the Ferrari F1-2000 are shown in Figure 7-4 on page 120 in chapter 7.

The front wing of the F1-2000 operates in ground effect and is so sensitive to it that the front axle downforce increases by more than

20 percent as the front ride height reduces from 25mm to zero. It is able to go to less than zero as the bodywork at the front axle is above the plane used to reference the ride height.

The rear axle downforce, however, has a definite optimum region at around 25mm ride height and falls off when the front height goes below 15mm. This combination of characteristics results in a shift of balance towards the front as the front height reduces, tempered slightly by the rear height reducing as well. The overall balance is rear biased compared to the weight distribution (around 35 to 38 percent front for the downforce, compared to 43 to 45 percent forward weight distribution). The reasons for this apparent imbalance are possibly twofold. The rear tyres have been too small since the FIA limited their width to 380mm, compared to 355mm for the front (48 percent of the available tyre width is possible on the front). Formula 1 cars have struggled to maintain a bal-

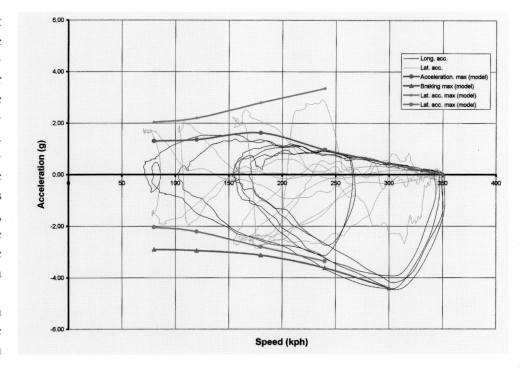

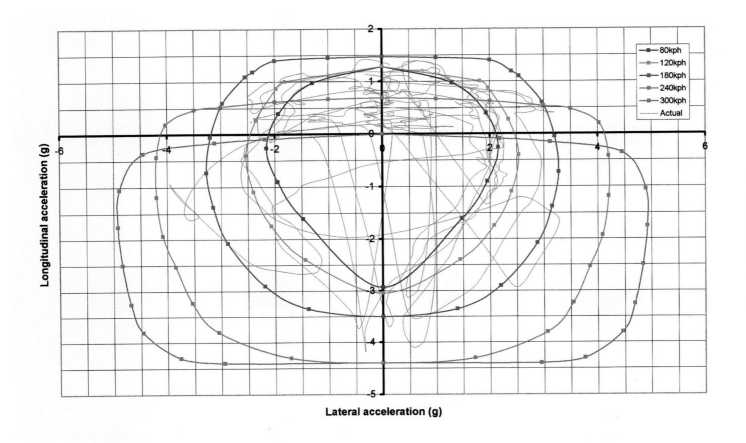

Longitudinal acceleration (g)

Lateral acceleration (g)

■	80kph
■	120kph
■	180kph
■	240kph
■	300kph
	Actual

LEFT: *[Fig. 14-13] Plotting Schumacher's g-g data from his qualifying lap of Imola (high downforce) on the MMM model's g-g data gives some indication of how Schumacher is able to use the potential performance. There are not many parts of the envelope that he is not able to exploit (there are no limit corners at Imola above around 180kph).*

RIGHT: *[Fig. 14-14] Plotting Schumacher's g-g data from his qualifying lap of Monza (low downforce) on the MMM model's g-g data gives some indication of how Schumacher is able to use the potential performance. As with Imola, there are not many parts of the envelope that he is not able to exploit, within the limitations set by the circuit. Particularly impressive is his ability to take the car right out into the braking/cornering quadrants, where the car is in its least stable state.*

ance throughout the speed range, and it is the tyre imbalance that has pushed weight distribution forward. Biasing the downforce to the rear will help the situation.

Additionally, the inherent stability of a car reduces with speed. Thus, as the speed increases and the downforce starts to dominate, the rear bias will counteract the natural reduction in stability.

It might appear to be logical to try and hold the car at 25mm rear ride height, limiting the forward movement of the overall downforce. However, examination of the drag map shows that minimum drag occurs when the rear ride height is as low as possible, and therefore it is desirable to attain a

low rear ride height at the top speed of the car. Nearly 10 percent drag reduction is possible if the rear of the car is practically on the ground, compared to the drag when it is at its highest ride height. The rear axle rising as the brakes are applied increases the drag beneficially.

The top speed range across the circuits on which Formula 1 cars race was 290 to 350kph in 2000, with the 800+ bhp available. The increase in power with speed, due to ram induction, as discussed earlier, enters the computation of top speed. Obviously, higher top speeds are possible with reduced downforce and drag, but these figures have been arrived at as providing the optimum aerodynamic charac-

teristics for minimum lap time, computed in lap simulations and confirmed in testing. The qualifying cornering speeds may be compromised for the race to achieve higher top speed to enable overtaking. Intelligence concerning the set-up and top speed of competitors enters the equation for determining race settings.

Table 7-2, and Figures 7-5 and 7-6 in chapter 7 show the compromises available to the race engineers of the F1-2000 when setting wings. Keeping the balance constant, the most efficient set-up is when the top speed comes out at 330kph.

The analysis for the performance envelope was carried out for two aerodynamic set-ups: maximum downforce, as used at Monaco, and maximum top speed, as used at Monza and Hockenheim. The change in shape and size of the resulting g-g-V diagrams illustrates the range of performance settings built into the car.

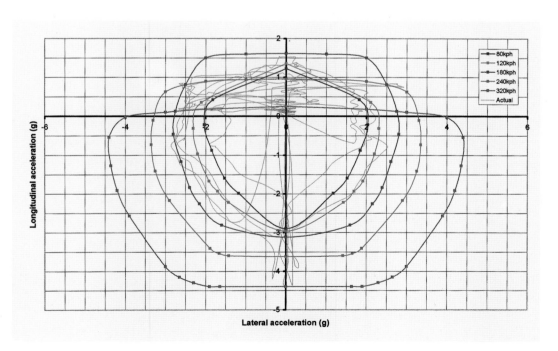

TYRES.

Figures 14-3 and 14-4 on page 190 show the normalised lateral force against slip angle characteristics of Bridgestone's 2000 Formula 1 tyres, front and rear. The curves are plotted for a tyre pressure of 1.36bar (20psi) and 0.5 degrees camber at three vertical loads. Figures 14-5 and 14-6 on page 191 are plots of normalised lateral load against longitudinal load, at one vertical load and a range of slip angles. The data is measured on a tyre test machine and serves mainly to illustrate the shape of the curves. Due to imperfect simulation of the track surface on the test machines and difficulties in maintaining constant tyre temperature and wear throughout a test, the absolute magnitude of the characteristics is not necessarily an accurate representation of those experienced on the track.

As detailed in chapter 13, Ferrari used a fully instrumented car to measure tyre characteristics on track, using the car as a form of tyre dynamometer. With knowledge of all the loads at each wheel, the slip angle and the slip ratio, camber, and tyre temperature, the techniques for measuring tyre characteristics under real conditions are improving all the time. Ferrari supplied corrections for the rig data for input into the performance envelope modelling. However, it is the tyre characteristics that provide one of the greatest uncertainties in this type of modelling.

SUSPENSION.

Without precise tyre characteristics for all loads, cambers, and pressures, there is little to be gained by using all the kinematics and compliance characteristics of the suspension in the model, even if they were available. What is important, however, is to model the attitude of the car and its aerodynamic surfaces under all loading conditions. To do this, suspension and tyre stiffness are required. The precise ways the suspension stiffens with load (rising rate springs and geometry) were not supplied by Ferrari, and so this introduces a further uncertainty.

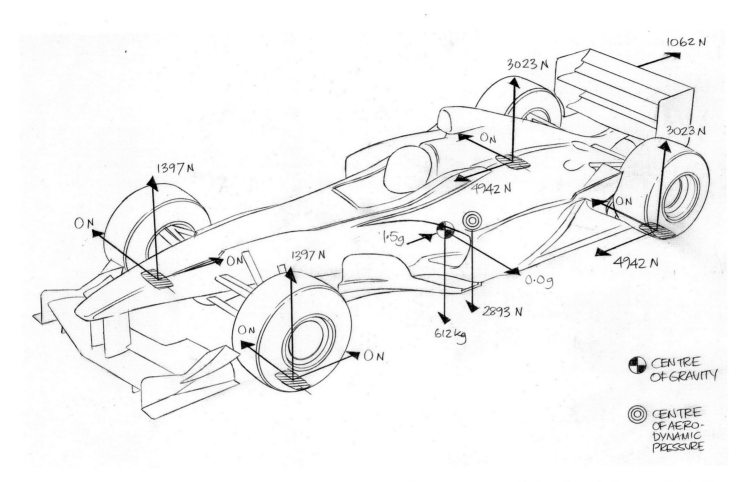

1062 N

3023 N

3023 N

1397 N

0 N

4942 N

0 N

0 N

1397 N

1.5g

4942 N

0 N

0.0g

0 N

2893 N

612 kg

0 N

⊕ CENTRE
OF GRAVITY

◎ CENTRE
OF AERO-
DYNAMIC
PRESSURE

LEFT: *[Fig. 14-15] The loads on the car and each tyre contact patch, as it accelerates at 1.5g and 150kph.*

TOP RIGHT: *[Fig. 14-16] The loads on the car and each tyre contact patch under maximum braking of 4.4g at 320kph.*

BOTTOM RIGHT: *[Fig. 14-17] Schumacher's qualifying lap of Monza—a 1:23.85 lap, which earned him pole position. Speed and longitudinal and lateral accelerations are plotted against distance around the lap.*

MODELS.

The model used for the performance analysis was developed and applied by Milliken Research Associates, Inc. (MRA). (Ref 14.3). Established in 1976, MRA is a small group of experienced engineers specializing in automobile stability and control, handling, associated tyre mechanics, automobile aerodynamics, and other related areas that come under the generalised heading of "vehicle dynamics."

MRA MOMENT METHOD (MMM).

MMM is a non-linear quasi-steady-state analysis that predicts vehicle handling over the full lateral and longitudinal acceleration range, including limit behaviour. MMM has many parallels to the static analysis of stability and control widely used in aircraft design.

Unlike time-based simulations, MMM constructs a portrait of the entire vehicle manoeuvring envelope by setting the vehicle at combinations of vehicle sideslip angle and steer angle. Constraining D'Alembert forces hold the vehicle in place—these forces and moments represent the unbalanced forces and moments available for linearly and angularly accelerating the vehicle. At each sideslip and steer combination, more than 100 detailed vehicle outputs are recorded.

Force-moment analysis, embodied in the MRA moment

method, has its roots in a 1952 Cornell Aeronautical Laboratories memo by Bill Milliken. It is an analysis based on the assumption that most stability and control characteristics of interest to the automotive engineer can be obtained from a study of the steady-state forces and moments on the vehicle. These forces and moments are those associated both with equilibrium (balanced) conditions as well as the "unbalanced" forces and moments available for linearly or angularly accelerating the vehicle (i.e., for stability and control).

ANALYSIS.

Of all the set-up options available to the race engineers for configuring a Formula 1 car for a given circuit, it is the lift/drag ratio that has the biggest effect on the performance envelope. For this reason, two aerodynamic set-ups have been modelled—maximum downforce and maximum top speed (which is also minimum downforce). Weight,

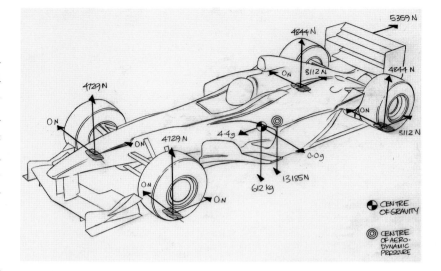

which is a function of fuel load, also has a major influence on the performance, but in order to establish the maximum potential performance, modelling was carried out at qualifying weight, i.e., 600kg plus minimum fuel.

Using the car and tyre parameters as described above, a number of acceleration and braking levels for each of five speeds were modelled using MMM and the maximum trimmed lateral acceleration output. The moment diagram—see Figure 14-7 on page 192 and Ref 14.2 for a complete explanation of the Moment Diagram—calculates the unbalanced forces and moments for a range of vehicle slip angles and steer angles, such that the controllable limit can be determined by inspection. These are plotted in Figures 14-8 and 14-9 on page 193.

MMM does not account for power limits on acceleration or for brake effort limits on deceleration. The first can be calculated and applied to the curves; the second can only be established by inspection of track data to arrive at the maximum braking that can be achieved by a driver. If speed is plotted on the Z-axis, the result is the g-g-V diagram (Figures 14-2 on page 189 and 14-10 on page 194). Interpolating between the calculated points permits the surface defining the limits of the potential performance of the car to be defined.

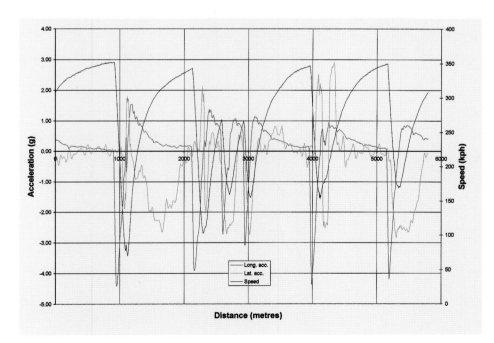

To look at the loads and certain other key parameters that describe the state of the car in a given condition, the appropriate point representing that condition is selected on the moment diagram, and the desired parameters are output. These have been used to illustrate what the car is doing under maximum acceleration, braking, and cornering and during the critical combined acceleration conditions.

VALIDATION.

The model results are useful only if they represent the performance of the car on the track. The g-g-V diagram represents one combination of car set-up, tyre, track, and environmental conditions, but should be reasonably close to actual track results. As the diagram represents the potential performance, it would be expected that its results would exceed the actual results by some margin, dependent on the handling characteristics of the car and the skill of the driver. The Ferrari F1-2000 is about as good as a 2000 Formula 1 car gets, and when Michael Schumacher drives a qualifying lap, the skill level is close to the limits of a human driver. Differences between the model output and actual data represent either inaccurate input data for the actual comparative conditions or limits of the man-machine combination to achieve the maximum potential performance. Most racing drivers can brake, accelerate, and corner at the maximum g-levels the car can generate, and so comparisons of these figures should show close agreement.

A plot of lateral and longitudinal acceleration against speed for a Michael Schumacher qualifying lap on a maximum downforce circuit (Imola) and a maximum top-speed circuit (Monza) and then superimposing the values calculated for discrete speeds by the model illustrates the level of matching for the peak values of acceleration, braking, and cornering (Figures 14-11 and 14-12 on pages 194 and 195, respectively). The peak values match well at low and medium speeds and

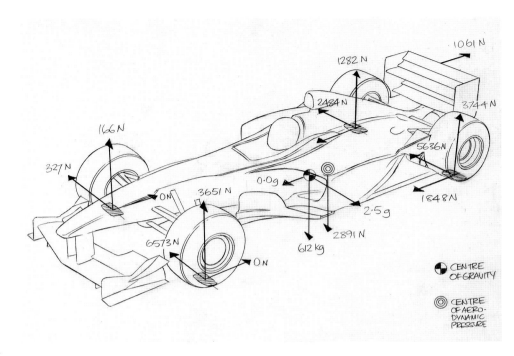

over-estimate at high cornering speeds.

A plot of the track data on the 2-D g-g diagram generated by the model (using the 3-D g-g-V diagram is visually confusing) illustrates that the driver is unwilling or unable to use the potential of the full performance envelope under a heavy combination of braking and cornering and, to a lesser extent, under acceleration and cornering (Figures 14-13 and 14-14 on pages 196 and 197, respectively).

PERFORMANCE.

While the actual maximum performance of the car on a real track is generally of most interest to those who follow motor racing, understanding why the full potential is not used, particularly entering a corner under braking and accelerating out again, is of interest to vehicle engineers trying to understand the performance of a Formula 1 car.

ACCELERATION.

The only time a Formula 1 car accelerates from a standstill, in earnest, is at the start of a race when it is fully fuelled and has cold tyres. On some circuits it will accelerate, almost in

ABOVE: *[Fig. 14-18] The loads on the car and each tyre contact patch when cornering at 120kph and 2.5g.*

RIGHT: *[Fig. 14-19] The loads on the car and each tyre contact patch when cornering at 240kph and 4.0g.*

a straight line, from speeds as low as 100kph under maximum performance conditions (e.g., low fuel and hot tyres). Thus, it is necessary to use both track data and calculation to arrive at 0 to 100kph and standing start quarter-mile elapsed times. For the Ferrari F1-2000, these figures are estimated to be:

0-100kph:	ET:	2.8 seconds
Standing start quarter-mile	ET:	8.8 seconds
	Terminal speed	297kph

 Acceleration is traction limited to around 150kph (higher on some low-grip tracks) and power limited above that speed. The peak acceleration at 150kph is 1.5g. Straight-line acceleration, at speeds below the power limit, is the one characteristic that is hurt by the quest for a lower centre of gravity height. For pure traction, the maximum load transfer onto the rear wheels is required. Traction also is one characteristic that limits the forward-biased weight dis-

tribution that has occurred since rear tyre width was limited by the regulations.

It may be surprising that the 0 to 100kph time is not so superior to a high-performance road car. With any car whose initial acceleration from a standstill is traction limited, power and weight do not come into the equation, and downforce has little benefit at these very low speeds. The rear tyre grip and rearward weight transfer determine acceleration. The Formula 1 car's tyres should be better than the road car's, provided they are up to their working temperature, but load transfer onto the rear axle will be much less, due to the significantly lower C of G height.

The condition of the car at peak acceleration is shown in Figure 14-15 on page 198.

BRAKING.
Examination of the data from Schumacher's qualifying lap at Monza in 2000 (Figure 14-17 on page 199) shows that he attains around 4.4g deceleration twice during the lap, indicating that this is probably the maximum useable. Just over 1g of this deceleration will be caused by aerodynamic drag. The loads on the car under this condition are illustrated in Figure 14-16 on page 199.

Development of brakes and tyres since 2000 has raised the maximum braking to consistently more than 5g.

Quoting 100 to 0kph figures for the braking performance of a Formula 1 car does not make a lot of sense, as this is not a manoeuvre a driver would normally make while racing, except in an emergency avoidance manoeuvre. However, it is possible to quantify braking performance by noting that it takes Michael Schumacher just 1.0 second to reduce speed by 100kph, from 250kph down to 150kph, and that he starts his braking for a 100kph corner, from 300kph, just more than 100 metres before the apex.

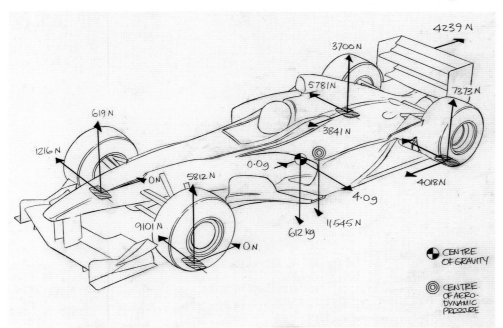

MAXIMUM CORNERING.

Modern Grand Prix circuits have been developed to embody a range of cornering speeds from 100 to 250kph, with true first-gear hairpins and very high-speed corners only occurring at a few exceptional circuits, such as Monaco and Spa, respectively. To illustrate the range of loads on the car at the maximum cornering acceleration it experiences, Figure 14-18 on page 200 and Figure 14-19 on page 201 show the Ferrari in 120kph and 2.5g and 240kph and 4g corners, just before the driver applies power to accelerate out of them.

Peak cornering acceleration will be achievable when the car is neutral at the limit and the tyres on the two axles are all at their individual limits. While this is difficult to achieve for the two tyres on an axle, due to compromises of suspension kinematics and load distribution, it should be possible to balance the front and rear axles. To manage this is a matter of the settings for aerodynamic balance, weight distribution, roll-stiffness distribution, tyre pressures, differential settings, and numerous other suspension set-up details. It will probably not be possible to achieve this balance for all speeds and conditions, especially for all track camber and elevation changes. The MMM model was set up to achieve as near as possible Schumacher's desired ideal—neutral handling characteristics.

TURN-IN.

Turning into a corner while braking from high speed is one of the manoeuvres that differentiates one car from another. Quite apart from the sudden contracting of the maximum g-limits as speed falls off sharply while the car is in the combined braking and cornering quadrant of the g-g-V diagram, it is likely to be set up to be marginally stable. If the car is set up to be too stable at the limit in this region, the driver will not be able to turn in while braking hard; if it is unstable, any bump or disturbance will try and spin the car. Apart from the

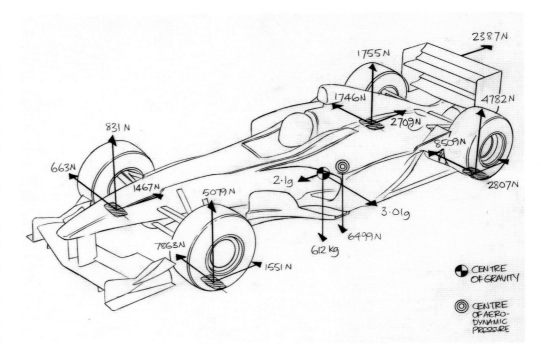

normal balance adjustments, such as weight and downforce distribution, which affect the balance under all conditions, the differential setting and the brake balance have major effects on the stability and control while braking and cornering together. The first is under the control of the active differential software, and for the second, the driver is able to fine-tune the brake distribution. Ferrari gave its drivers this control at their fingertips to ensure it could always be set to their liking.

Hard braking and turn-in to corners are the sections where the greatest difference shows up between a qualifying lap and routine test running. It is the manoeuvre where time can be made up, but at the greatest risk of spinning off or at the best, losing time by running wide. It also takes place on parts of the track where overtaking another driver is most likely. Thus the set-up of the car for these conditions is not only critical in handling terms, but it may determine the result of both qualifying and the race. It also is the region of the g-g-V

ABOVE: [Fig. 14-20] The loads on the car and each tyre contact patch when turning in at 180kph, braking at 2.1g, and cornering at 3.04g. For this case, the brake balance is set up to make the car neutral at the limit.

RIGHT: *[Fig. 14-21] The loads on the car and each tyre contact patch when turning in at 180kph, braking at 2.1g, and cornering at 2.97g. For this case, the brake balance is 5 percent more to the front, with the result that the car understeers at the limit.*

BELOW: *[Fig. 14-22] The loads on the car and each tyre contact patch when turning in at 180kph, braking at 2.1g, and cornering at 2.93g. For this case, the brake balance is 5 percent more to the rear, with the result that the car oversteers at the limit.*

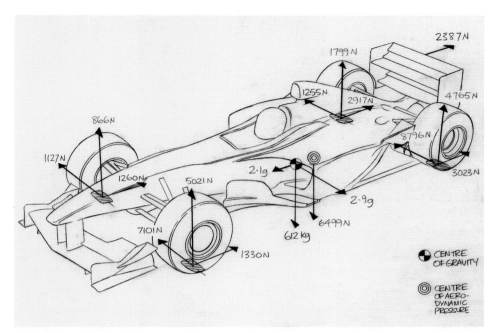

diagram where the driver seldom reaches the edge of the potential performance envelope. Using the output of the MMM model, it is possible to look in detail at what is happening on the car while the driver brings the speed down and sets up the car for a corner.

We will consider a point where the driver is braking hard for a corner: braking deceleration is down to 2.1g, lateral acceleration is 3.04g at this moment, and speed is 180kph. The loads on the car and tyres are shown in Figure 14-20. All four tyres are very near their peak grip for their individual vertical forces. The two inner tyres are not able to generate much lateral force as the brake torque dominates, while the outer two tyres carry most of the lateral force. Front and rear axles are just about equally near their limits, and the car is quite well balanced

in this condition.

The exact distribution of vertical loads will depend on the set-up of the car, particularly the weight, downforce, and roll-stiffness distributions. The braking torque at each wheel will depend on the brake balance and the configuration of the differential at that moment—probably locked. It is control of the brake balance that the driver of the F1-2000 has at his fingertips, and Figures 14-21 and 14-22 show what happens on the car, at this point in the lap, if he adjusts it 5 percent more to the front and rear, respectively.

With 5 percent more to the front, the front axle is on the limit at 2.97g, with the front tyres unable to generate any more lateral force. The driver thus is not only at the limit of cornering force, but also at the limit of control; the car is stable, however. To be able to influence the heading and hence the slip angle of the car, he must reduce braking. If he has left braking to the absolute last minute, he will inevitably overshoot the apex.

With 5 percent more braking to the rear, the rear axle is on the limit at 2.93g, and the car is unstable. Whether the driver can cope with this level of instability while braking and turning in will depend on his skill and other factors we will consider in a moment. Again, the driver must reduce brak-

ing to return the car to a stable condition, or he may spin on entry to the corner, a condition in which many drivers found themselves during 2000.

Whether the driver finds himself in this exact condition as he modulates the brake pedal force to compensate for the downforce reducing with speed will depend on many set-up details of the car and is way beyond the data available for this analysis. However, it does illustrate the delicate balance of the car under braking and turn-in to a corner. How the driver copes with it is partly a measure of his skill and bravery and partly a function of the dynamic characteristics of the car. Analysing the dynamic performance is even further beyond this quasi-static analysis. While the forces and moments on the car in any combination of speed and longitudinal and lateral acceleration can be calculated, the response of the vehicle to these forces and moments requires precise knowledge of the dynamic characteristics of the tyres, aerodynamics, chassis structure, dampers, and, most complex of all, the inputs of the driver. Disturbing bumps in the track

will further influence the response of the car, especially if the car is in an unstable state—Interlagos in Brazil is infamous for catching out drivers when braking and turning in, especially as the bumps change from year to year!

The greatest braking performance available from the car in this phase is when it is set up the nearest to neutral. It is also the time when the driver wants maximum control to turn in and set up the car for the corner, and an overly stable configuration will have him complaining of understeer on entry or the need to brake in a nearly straight line before trying to turn the car in. Too little stability will have the car turning in at the least provocation, with oversteer. It is not surprising that this sector of the g-g-V diagram is least exploited by drivers, as to use all the performance available requires a car that is, or is nearly, unstable. Without a computer to assist him (as pilots of relaxed-stability aircraft have in their fly-by-wire control systems), it comes down to driver skill and bravery again and details of the car's response. Factors such as moments of inertias, yaw damping, and tyre characteristics at their limit are all crucial to the response of the car, determining how close to the limit, defined by stability, the driver is prepared to venture.

Before judging a driver's performance in utilising the full braking and turn-in performance of a car and his ability to track the outer boundary of the g-g-V diagram, one should try and visualise what it takes to control a marginally stable car at the limits of its performance, as it tracks the edge of the performance envelope contracting from nearly 4.5g at 350kph to just 2.0g at 80kph in 3.5 seconds. This is what happens while braking for the first chicane at Monza. The rate at

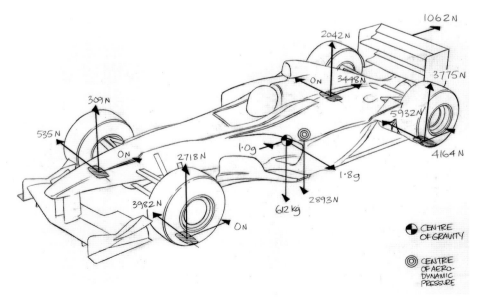

1062N
2042N
0N
3448N
3775N
309N
5932N
535N
0N
1.0g
4164N
2718N
1.8g
3982N
612kg
2893N
0N

CENTRE OF GRAVITY

CENTRE OF AERO-DYNAMIC PRESSURE

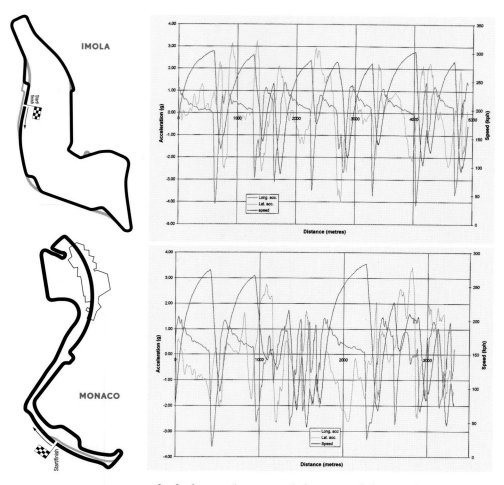

IMOLA

MONACO

which the conditions and the state of the car change probably set the limits of how close to the edge a driver can go.

Marco Fainello states in chapter 13, "We know that in theory we could have a set-up that is much, much faster than what we are using, but that the driver would not be able to drive it." A great deal of research is going into understanding the performance and characteristics of the car in the braking-turning phase and establishing the dynamic performance of its components and systems. As the understanding increases, including a greater understanding of the driver, there will be subtle changes to the car and tyres, probably invisible to all but the most tutored eye. There is no doubt, however, that this is an area where Ferrari and Bridgestone are putting a great deal of effort, and their results in recent years reflect this.

CORNER EXIT.

Following turn-in, when the driver is completely off the brakes and has the car settled into the constant radius section of the corner around the apex, he must apply power to maintain speed, overcoming aerodynamic drag and the power absorbed by the tyres as they generate lateral forces. With left-foot braking, the transition from braking to power-on can be very smooth, with minimum unsettling of the car. Depending on the speed and set-up of the car, power may create either understeer, due either to the differential set-up or by the load transfer front to rear, or cause oversteer, due to reducing the grip available for cornering from the rear axle. Adjusting the power to maintain the turning rate of the car is a skill learned by the youngest kart racer, and increasing it to gain maximum acceleration as the corner radius increases again and the cornering force reduces is as much an issue of car set-up and performance as driver skill. Since 2001, when traction control was reintroduced, even this performance factor was passed from the driver to the software and race engineers. However, in 2000, the Ferrari drivers relied on their own skill, as well as the characteristics of the car.

Figure 14-23 shows the modelled outputs for the F1-2000 accelerating out of a corner at 120kph, with 1.8g lateral and 1.0g longitudinal acceleration. It is traction limited, rather than power limited at this speed, and will oversteer at the limit.

The above "snapshots" of the F1-2000 give a very limited description of the complexity of the performance characteristics of a modern Formula 1 car. Full analysis is only available to the engineers responsible for the cars, and even they may not have the full picture. In the end, in spite of the massive number-crunching simulations and the hundreds of measurements taken over thousands of kilometres of testing, it is the stopwatch that records the only performance indicator that actually counts in motor racing.

15

Racing and Development

F1-2000 development.

*T*he car with which Ferrari started the 2000 season was one
that Technical Director Ross Brawn felt was capable of taking the
challenge to McLaren, rather than having to try and keep up. The
previous year, Ferrari won the Manufacturers' Championship but
failed to win the Drivers' Championship because of Michael Schumacher's accident mid-season,
which forced Ferrari to transfer its main effort to their number two, Eddie Irvine. However,
Brawn feels that they were playing catch-up throughout the season: "The car was not good

LEFT: *United States Grand Prix,
Indianapolis. Michael Schumacher
first, Rubens Barichello second. In
spite of a spin by Schumacher, this
was a straight forward 1-2 in front of
the all-important American fans.
Beating Hakkinen, whose engine
ultimately failed, was crucial to
Schumacher's World Championship.*

RIGHT: *Ignazio Lunetta, Race
Engineering Team Leader.*

enough in either '98 or '99, and we were desperate for
Michael's input to enable us to be competitive."

To mount a serious challenge for the championships in
Formula 1 requires a combination of factors: a car that is
fundamentally fast on a variety of circuits, from Monaco,
to Monza, to Spa; the ability to set up and gain the maximum
from the cars at a given circuit during a Grand Prix event; two
fast and experienced drivers; reliability; flexible race strategies; and a reasonable measure of luck. With the budgets and
resources that the major teams have nowadays, this would
seem to be straight-forward to achieve, but Brawn believes
that it was not until 2000 that Ferrari had all the elements

ready at the first race in Melbourne, Australia. Schumacher
won the first three races, gaining a substantial points advantage over Mika Hakkinen and David Coulthard in their
initially unreliable McLarens. He was able to maintain that
advantage through to mid-season when a series of three
races, in which Schumacher failed to gain a single point,
shook Ferrari and tested its strength of character to the
full. Hakkinen's motivation was stimulated by Ferrari's
problems, and he took over the lead in the championship in
Hungary. However, four straight wins in the last four races
enabled Schumacher to take the championship by the 20
points he had gained over Hakkinen in the first two races,

before McLaren had managed to score (Figure 15-3).

Ross Brawn recalls the mood at the Scuderia at the beginning of the 2000 season: "In previous years, we got to the first race and found we were half a second or so off the pace and thought, 'Oh my God, what are we going to do about it?' To the team's credit, they really did a fantastic job to make the cars competitive and able to mount a challenge with Michael. For the first time, in Australia in 2000, we thought, 'Right, at least we are starting on a pretty good footing; we are competitive; we can build on this; now we can move forward.'"

Michael Schumacher also agrees that the F1-2000 was the best car or close to being the best car of the field, whereas before this was not so. "In previous years, we had to rely on our teamwork and efforts, and make the best job we could," Schumacher says. "Then in 2000 we had the car as well, which, combined with our efforts, had the performance of the others. I knew the car was good as soon as I sat in it and drove it. It was so easy to distinguish that it was different from the previous car, right away. You feel it immediately when you drive a good car."

Schumacher is at pains to disabuse people of the notion that the cars are designed to suit him. "People often say, or may even believe, that the engineers would build a car to suit a driving style, but this doesn't really exist. They build their best knowledge into the car and the driver just gets on with it. The aerodynamics so affect the performance of the car that previous experiences with Ross and Rory, such as with Benetton in '94 and '95, don't have much influence on current designs, which are now developed in a proper wind tunnel. The group, chassis and engine, has grown together and now has a consistent base. The one hand is working with the other, rather than not knowing what the other is doing."

Brawn recounts how the momentum flowed during the season: "It was not a particularly difficult car to operate; it was relatively easy to set up, but it was undoubtedly stronger

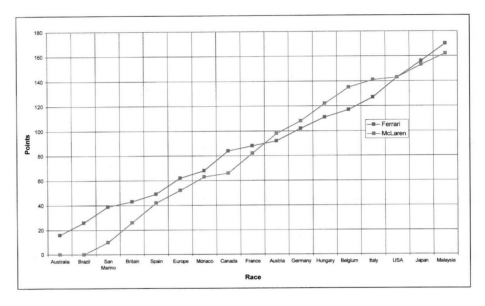

at some circuits than others. We had a tendency to be better at high downforce and low- to medium-speed circuits, than very low downforce and high-speed circuits, in spite of the fact that we won Monza that year. We were not so good at circuits with lots of high-speed corners, such as Barcelona and Spa. Spa was a tricky race, as it had always been a circuit where we had struggled and we had never been truly competitive. We were at a bit of a low point in the season when Spa came round—we had just had five races in which we had scored 10 points, which for a World Championship is not good enough—so the fact that we nearly won the race was encouraging. We almost beat McLaren at a track where they had always beaten us, and I took a lot of encouragement from Spa and tried to pass that on down to our people by saying, 'Look, this was traditionally our worst circuit of the year, and we almost did it, so I think we can still do this thing.' The last four races of the year were just fantastic from a racing point of view. Spa was the watershed."

Mid-season is when championships are often won or lost, as the Formula 1 circus grinds its way across Europe from

Magny Cours to Monza. Maintaining superiority or recovering from a car deficit just as the race teams wear themselves out travelling, racing, and rebuilding the cars between races is the real test of the organisation. Ferrari hit problems in this period in 2000, just as McLaren and Hakkinen upped their game.

Recalled Brawn: "Around Austria/Germany time, we had quite a few difficult meetings as we had fallen behind in the championship, from some 20-odd points ahead to being behind. In some ways we were trying too hard. We had been dominant in the early part of the season, where before we had always been playing catch-up; we had suddenly been

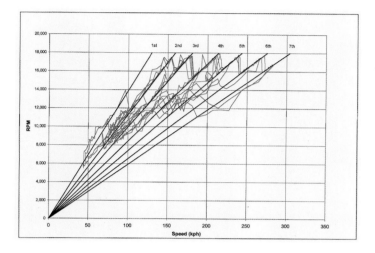

LEFT: *[Fig. 15-3] This chart plots the Manufacturers' Championship points acquired by the leading contenders, Ferrari and McLaren, race by race. It shows just how close the contest was in 2000.*

NEAR RIGHT: *Technical Director Ross Brawn is in constant communication with his drivers during a race.*

ABOVE RIGHT: *[Fig. 15-5] This data is for Schumacher's qualifying lap at Monaco. Plotting rpm (indicating rear wheel speed) against speed (measured at the front wheels) will display the gear ratios, provided the wheels do not slip. Where the rpm trace has a value greater than the gear ratio line, wheel spin is occurring; where below, the front wheels are locking. Wheel spin occurs in all gears up to and including fourth.*

in front and we didn't know how to deal with it. I felt a bit wobbly at that stage!

"I decided that we would stop trying to throw new innovations at the car to try and solve our problems, we would just do the job properly with what we already had. We could all see that we had a tool that could do the job, and we were not using it properly. A racing car is not necessarily about getting the theoretical maximum out of it at a race weekend, it is about getting the achievable maximum, and that is very different. You go to a track and do two days of testing/practice, including qualifying, and you have to race the car on the Sunday. You are better off getting 95 percent every day of the week than getting 90 percent one day and 99 percent another. It is something we went too far on with the 2000 car and had to come back on."

That the F1-2000 was, on average, as quick or quicker than the McLaren MP4-15 is beyond doubt, but Brawn is quite clear where its strengths and weaknesses lay when compared to the McLaren. He gives full credit to Paolo Martinelli and his engine group for the steady development of the 049 engine through the year, until it surpassed the Mercedes engine in the McLaren.

"By the end of the season, we had a much better engine,"

Brawn says. "Paolo was able to give us more power in qualifying for the last few races, and Michael was on pole for the last four. Paolo and his people did a super job, finding that extra power. Qualifying is so important strategically; it makes for a positive approach to the whole planning of the race. We know from an engineer who joined us from McLaren at the end of the season that they were quite perplexed. We were pretty well matched at the start of the season, and then we were able to move ahead on power."

The ability of the F1-2000 to put down its power and the ease with which its drivers were able to control wheel spin and oversteer led inevitably to accusations of bending the traction control regulations. Some of Ferrari's nearest competitors also levelled charges that the FIA was allowing them to get away with it.

Brawn emphatically refutes those charges. "You have to judge it by what happened later, in 2001, when traction control was permitted. Nothing changed in terms of relative competitiveness! It was a difficult situation because we were pushing the boundaries of what was perceived to be traction control with the engine control system. We were in daily negotiation with the FIA as to what they would accept.

LEFT: *Michael Schumacher, the master of detail, studies the TAG-Heuer timing display.*

RIGHT: *Ten seconds of synchronised action are all that is required to fit four new wheels and tyres and add 100 litres of fuel.*

They found it difficult, because when we presented them with the information on complex engine dynamics, it was difficult for them to fully understand what was going on. You push the boundaries as hard as you can—it is part of the job. We would sit around the table with the FIA's specialists, make presentations and discuss things. We never had a closed-loop traction control system; it would have been obvious and we couldn't do it. However, we had ways in which we tried to keep the engine as driveable as possible. There were some physical things we did, like the twin throttles and fuel phasing, which were things that helped prevent the engine running away with itself. There was never any situation where the driver could stand on the throttle and things would take care of themselves. If the driver smoothly applied the throttle, the engine would behave itself nicely and it wouldn't get out of control, while that wasn't the case a few years ago. Back then you had to modulate the throttle because the torque wasn't even. We were able to produce a nice smooth torque curve with engine management that a driver could operate progressively."

Schumacher gives his view on the engine's power delivery characteristics: "The driveability of the engine is not so important for one lap, but for a race distance it is very important. If you have a spike of power, you will simply spin the wheels, and that creates tyre temperature and causes the rubber to wear much quicker. It is something the driver has to get involved with the development and testing of, as only he can give the correct feedback."

LEFT: *One of the most heart-stopping moments in Grand Prix racing—the standing start. This is Japan in 2000, with the leading contenders for the drivers' title, Michael Schumacher and Mika Hakkinen, hurtling neck and neck into the first corner. Hakkinen won the corner, but Schumacher won the race and took the title.*

RIGHT: *Team Manager Stefano Domenicali, upon whose shoulders lie the logistics and organisation of seventeen races in eight months, held all over the world.*

In the absence of any protests against Ferrari in 2000, one can only examine the evidence and listen to the people actually involved. Analysis of data from Schumacher's qualifying laps at a number of circuits, especially Monaco where traction control would be a real advantage, indicates that accelerating out of slow corners the wheels spin (Figure 15-5 on page 209). In any gear, there should be an almost fixed relationship between engine rpm and speed, measured by the front wheel sensor. It will not be absolutely constant, but should only vary by the slip ratio if it is to be kept at or below the limit. The data indicates this is so under most circumstances, but not when accelerating hard in low gears up to third and occasionally in higher gears over bumps. If traction control was fitted, it didn't work. What Ferrari evidently did have was an extremely sophisticated throttle control and engine management system that gave the driver more precise control over a peaky 800 hp racing engine in a 600kg car than ever before.

"There was always the perception that we were getting special treatment from the FIA," Brawn recalls, "but in fact we were just talking to them more than anyone else. We were doing more. With the two test tracks we have, and the three departments—chassis, engine, and electronics—that are here close together, we are talking every day about it [driveability improvements] and go out on the track and try it. It was a key area of car performance, and we were doing things all the time. Within the constraints of the regulations, we probably had the best system of controlling the engine and hence driveability. It was very much a track-orientated system—you couldn't really simulate it or do it on a dynamometer, you had to get out on the track, and Fiorano is great for that sort of testing. With all the electronic and software systems, we are very strong because we are here, testing six days a week, getting the things to work. Having come from an English team where that didn't exist, I now wonder how they manage there, because I can't envisage doing it without the test tracks."

The problem that faced Ferrari mid-season, whereby the F1-2000's appetite for rear tyres became a limiting factor on circuits with predominately high-speed corners, turned out to be a fundamental design problem. Brawn says, "The weakness exhibited on high-speed corners was a rear suspension problem. Over the winter we developed a new rear suspension, and in retrospect we had made a classic mistake, because we had developed it in the cold conditions of win-

ter, and we didn't pick up on the fact that we were putting a little bit more energy into the rear tyres. It sounds very easy and fundamental now, but you go winter testing, you put a bit more energy into the tyre, and it looks as if it is working better, because in the winter you are struggling for temperature. Then, when we went racing, we didn't see it initially, because we were competitive and McLaren wasn't. But, by the time we got to Magny Cours, we couldn't keep the rear tyre together, and they beat us because they could make much better use of the rear tyre. Around that time we started to backtrack, because it seemed to me that we were in a worse condition than we had been in before. We were looking at rear tyres: geometry, camber change, damping—all those things started to be re-examined to see whether we could touch it, change it. An obvious thing we could do was to put on the old suspension, because it was there; we could just bolt it straight on. Almost straight away we saw a step in the right direction, in terms of reducing rear tyre temperature and increasing their durability. The main difference was geometry—camber change.

"We were also playing around a lot with the radiator air exits on the bodywork," Brawn continues. "We thought that where we were exiting the radiator air was heating the tyre up, and so we copied McLaren and came up with the 'funnel' to lift the hot air coming out of the radiators away from the rear tyre. We had a bit of evidence that we had been exacerbating the problem with the hot air."

There was a perception at the time that Bridgestone had come to the rescue of Ferrari by providing tyres to help overcome its rear tyre durability problems, under the guise of starting to develop tyres for the following year, when Michelin was to enter the arena. More competitive compounds were tested and raced in the last few events, but these were developed to suit the McLaren as well as the Ferrari (it was not clear at that stage which would take the

championship). The rear suspension change had already partially solved the problem.

Brawn says, "In the end, we discovered, through simulation, that the stiffness of the suspension—that is, camber stiffness and toe stiffness, not so much vertical stiffness—seemed to be inadequate on the 2000 car. We made a step change for 2001, putting around two kilograms on the unsprung mass—no small increase—and that car was much better on tyre durability. That was probably the other part of the problem."

One aspect of the car where McLaren was better than Ferrari, visible to anyone watching the cars, was in the ability to ride kerbs. "Their approach seemed to be to have a soft car with suspension travel," says Brawn of his championship rivals, "which enabled them to ride the kerbs much better than we could. Hockenheim, for instance, is a kerb-riding circuit. Although Rubens won the race under strange circumstances, when a disgruntled Mercedes employee got onto the track and disrupted the race, up to that point McLaren were disappearing. We did a lot of work on kerb riding after that and it got better. By Monza we had found some set-up options, which enabled us to take the chicanes much better; that is such an important aspect on so many circuits nowadays."

SET-UP.

The job of racing a Formula 1 car on seventeen race circuits around the world, each with a different combination of fast, medium, and slow corners, straights, elevation, track surface, and local climate, requires a different technical approach from that needed to design and develop an effective race car in the first place. Ross Brawn spans both disciplines, able to lead both the design and manufacture of the tool and then use of it. The engineers and mechanics that take the cars racing are, however, a different breed from those who

Michael Schumacher flashes over the line at Suzuka to become the first driver to win the World Championship in a Ferrari for 21 years.

spend all their time at the factory. Apart from the travel and long hours, they must be adaptable, able to think on their feet, and be prepared to take calculated risks if circumstances demand it. Motor racing success used to come to those best able to manufacture their own luck, but Ferrari has striven to take the luck element out of racing, though it is still an element that can contribute to the outcome of a race, either way.

Completing 300 or so kilometres of racing, faster than any other competitor, only can be achieved if all the elements are in place. Set-up for the circuit, choice of tyres, grid position, race strategy, pit work, reliability, and driving all contribute, but the basic competitiveness of a team is set before the cars leave the factory. Changes of form seldom come about due to activity at a race weekend, though races are often lost due to them. Brawn believes that it is essential to have a car that is easy to set up and tries to have every race at as high a performance level as possible in every respect. Any time they fail to have the cars set up properly is regarded as a big failure, and he strives to develop the organisation to have the car as strong as possible every time. As axiomatic as this may seem, so many other teams fail to achieve this that one wonders if they appreciate how important it is. Time spent in testing, trying to gain the tiniest fraction of a second with a new front wing or diffuser, is often better spent allowing the driver to get used to the car without changing it much and for the race engineers to refine their set-ups and gain experience of dialling the car in to a circuit quickly and reliably.

As has been shown earlier, a modern Formula 1 car needs a small army of engineers, technicians, and mechanics to run it, including those from the tyre, fuel, and electronics suppliers. Establishing the specification of the car for each run, whether it is in testing or at a race, and ensuring that the car is set up to that specification have become major clerical tasks for the race engineers and the Chief Mechanic. When the car does run, the flow of data from it is now so dense—

around 250 channels in 2000, rising to 1,000 in 2003—that is it beyond human capabilities to monitor and analyse it all quickly enough to influence the subsequent run. While computers monitor the health of systems, driver comments have to be assessed, interpreted, and compared, by humans, to the performance data. Expert software and specialists back at the factory, linked to the output from the car by satellite, assist in making the decisions necessary before running the car again. The flow of information and instructions based on those decisions has to be managed, and in the end mechanics have to be able to use ordinary tools to make changes to the car.

Ferrari's circuit database, carefully assembled over the past few years and allied to its continuously improving simulation techniques, has enabled it to arrive at most circuits with a set-up close to the optimum. Knowing the tyres that will be available is an essential part of this approach, and in 2000 when Bridgestone supplied tyres to the entire grid, the options were limited. Now, with tyres under continuous and intense development, it is necessary to have as much information about them, prior to the race, as is possible. Testing two weeks before an event, where possible on the actual track, generates the basic data to supplement rig characteristics. A meeting between Ferrari and Bridgestone, on the Wednesday before they arrive at the circuit, establishes the plan for the Friday and Saturday free practise periods.

Running time on the Friday and Saturday morning at each Grand Prix has to be shared between checking and fine-tuning the set-up of the cars and evaluating the tyre options. Once the tyre is chosen (for qualifying and the race), its race characteristics and durability can be assessed for input into the formulation of the race strategy. The tyres cannot be evaluated until the set-up is right, and time spent on making the car fast, to gain a good grid position, eats into the time for long runs on the chosen tyre with a rep-

The engine assembly shop, with V-10s being built and prepared for tests and races.

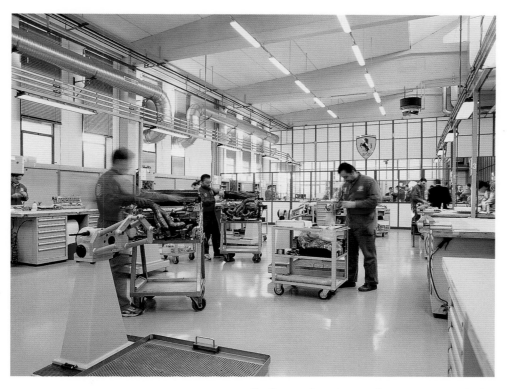

de Grint. "Ferrari takes that data and accepts it absolutely—which cannot be said for a number of the other teams. They do the tests correctly and believe the data and our calculations. This approach, based on complete trust, is the right one. We strive to make our predictions as accurate as possible, and Ferrari is confident in them for the development of their strategies."

One area of the car that has proven to be difficult to set up for a given circuit is the active differential. Explains Brawn: "We initially tried too hard, trying to get more out of it, and started to go backwards. We were developing some quite clever differential strategies, which when they were perfect were good, but it took three days at a test circuit to get them set up. We had to tune them individually for each corner and get the whole thing optimised everywhere—then it worked very well. Then you'd get a change of conditions and the thing would get upset. We were on too much of a knife edge. Because of the regulation constraints at that period, you were allowed some speed variation derived from engine rpm and the gear ratio, which were used to calculate engine torque, though you were not permitted to use car speed directly. Unfortunately, using the torque curve to derive car speed was not rigorous, and the system got confused at times. You had to be very careful how you managed it and not try to get too much out of the system. We were trying to optimise the differential for a particular corner, based on the calculated torque into the diff. You could get it right, but then it would trip you up somewhere else, because they were not unique points on the map of torque.

"I said to the engineers, 'OK, though there might be a few tenths of a second in all this, how often do we really see it?' You could see it at Fiorano and Mugello, because we were there every day of the week, but we weren't seeing it at races. So, we decided to keep it simple and introduced the philosophy of starting an event with a very flat differential

resentative race fuel weight. Ferrari has prioritised the available track time and developed a rigorous procedure for an event, which Ross Brawn ensures is stuck to under almost all circumstances.

Bridgestone engineer Kees van de Grint explains the team's approach at the track: "Ferrari comes to the circuit well prepared and then waits till the track is cleaned up and some rubber is put down. They see no point in running on a green circuit, as the results they would get would be wrong. I believe that their simulations are ahead of the opposition, and that enables Ross to stick to a plan. The car is nearly always well set up from the start, and that leaves more time for tyre comparisons.

"Bridgestone takes the data from the long runs on fuel and extrapolates to arrive at a predicted tyre durability, that is, a curve of lap time against number of laps run," continues van

"For me there is only one word to describe the ideal handling characteristic: 'neutral.'
In the end, I drive what is fastest for me, and I sort of work out what that is. It may be
different from what other drivers want."

map, with no specific features for particular speed ranges. What I wanted them to do was to get the car handling first. We know that the differential is a very key area of car handling, with its ability to distribute the torque between the two rear wheels and hence steer the car, but if you have two things you are trying to optimise together, you get confused. We didn't have good enough simulation tools then to tell us how to do it, so we said, 'Start on Friday morning with a flat differential map, get the car handling, and then, when it is well set up and all the normal, basic stuff has been exploited—roll bars, camber, etc.—then introduce some variances on the differential.' We started with the differential locking under braking and a fixed pressure under acceleration, with a ramp to smooth between the two. We soon found that that was almost what we would use the whole weekend; it's that difference between the theoretical maximum and achievable maximum again."

"The differential can easily confuse the driver," says Schumacher. "There are all sorts of things you can do with it; you can easily start at the wrong end and you will maybe never get it right. If you go the wrong way, you try to chase, being unable to fix the problem without knowing just what it is. Nowadays we start with a straightforward set-up and just fine-tune."

Schumacher is quite clear about what he wants from the handling characteristics of any racing car: "For me there is only one word to describe the ideal handling characteristic: 'neutral.' In the end, I drive what is fastest for me, and I sort of work out what that is. It may be different from what other drivers want. I guess you could say that there is some indication that I look for a more neutral car than some of the teammates I have had."

Schumacher is modest about the car control skills he possesses. A "neutral" car, while providing good response to steering inputs, has no natural stability. The driver must

make just the right inputs and be able to correct overshoots and undesired responses due to irregularities in the track. The car will not make the corrections for him. I suspect that it is this need to constantly correct an nearly unstable car, when driven at its limit that has led some observers to comment that Schumacher "appears to make his Ferrari dance."

RACE STRATEGY.

In this era of refuelling and tyre stops during Formula 1 races and the influence they have on races where the only major opportunities for overtaking are at the start and during pit stops, Ferrari's team of Ross Brawn and Michael Schumacher has emerged as the master of race strategy. It is a combination of methodical strategic analysis and planning, tactical risk taking, and superb execution. However, such is the nature of the game and the unpredictable nature of the other players that results do not always follow the plan. In 2000, the battle with McLaren was intense, with cars and lead drivers often evenly matched for sheer speed. Race strategy played as important a part in the outcome as the performances of car and driver.

Ross Brawn explains: "We made some mistakes in 2000; we had some races that didn't work out for us, but in general we were fortunate. Sometimes when you are behind and trying to attack you can afford to take a risk, but when you are in front and have to defend, it is more difficult. So often that year McLaren were in front, defending, and we were able to get them because they had to follow the conventional route. The other thing about that year was that there was no one behind us, so we were in second place and there wasn't a Williams behind us such that if we got it wrong we would finish in third place. It was McLaren and Ferrari, and even if we got it wrong we would still finish second. We were able to take a calculated risk on occasions, take different strategies. If it rained, we could come in early or even leave

The race shop, where all the cars are built and serviced between races. Each car is assigned to a service bay, where it is stripped after tests or races, and all parts are sent off to be checked and rebuilt as required.

the dry tyres on, something a little bit different."

With Ferrari, it is well known that Brawn makes the strategy in consultation with Schumacher. At McLaren, it is less clear to the observer exactly who decides on strategy and how it is done. "The way we operate is to do a thorough analysis of what we think is the right strategy, so over a race weekend we will have the tyre degradation number and we will have the effect of fuel. Of course, every track varies in the effect of fuel: it is as low as 0.025 seconds a lap per kilogram for Monza, to as high as 0.045 seconds a lap per kilogram for Spa. Tracks with medium- and high-speed corners are those where you are going to have a high fuel effect.

"You put all those numbers into a simulation," Brawn says, "and everyone has the same sort of simulation—it is quite a simple one—and that tells you, with the pit stop time and other factors, what is going to be the quickest race. Then you have to make a subjective judgement about overtaking, and you have to include certain factors, for example, it may not be the quickest way to race, but you cannot be overtaken because you are on pole and your start performance is good. You are entering the subjective area, which is down to experience. I will talk to Michael and ask him if he can overtake on this track. The car may not be very good and he will not want to risk it, so we will evolve a strategy in a different way. Or he will come back and say that the car is good and has good traction. He will have felt it on low downforce in the warm-up, and if it feels all right, he will say that he can have a go. It all goes into the decision on what to do.

"There is only so much you can do mathematically. I tend to get the opinion that McLaren rely mainly on mathematical models, and they try and develop an expert system. They probably have an overtaking coefficient and maybe a weather coefficient, all of which go into it, and then they get a number out and they follow it. Ninety percent of the time, they have a good sensible strategy, but it does appear that when they are faced by a change of circumstances, because they rely on a model rather than being prepared to make a judgement occasionally, they struggle a bit. Perhaps that is where we are a little bit more flexible."

Working with a driver of Schumacher's capabilities adds to the flexibility in executing race strategies. His ability to assess the situation, analysing it second by second while driving at the limit, and to carry out almost impossible tasks at Brawn's request, even driving at qualifying speeds for lap after lap if required, has contributed to the successes the pair has accomplished. Schumacher tends to play down his part in it, but Brawn is adamant that without Schumacher's contributions, their record of snatching victory from the jaws of defeat would be significantly diminished.

"You try and work out the strategy before the race," says Schumacher, "and sometimes alternatives. Sometimes you just have to react instinctively to the situation. Ross is the main person, sitting outside having the whole overview and giving me the information, which I then try to work with. We have been together for six years and know each other quite well.

"Sometimes we have to exchange information during a race and that may lead to a certain strategy, but I would say it is at least 90 percent his ability and job to take the decisions, because he has a much wider picture than I do, when in the car."

RELIABILITY.

In recent years, Ferrari has established and put in place what is necessary to achieve reliability in Formula 1. In 2000, Schumacher dropped out of races due to mechanical failures on only two occasions: an exhaust cracking at Monaco that led to suspension failure and an engine failure in France. With three retirements, Barrichello was less fortunate. He suffered an engine in Brazil, hydraulics problems in Britain, and low fuel pressure in Belgium; some suggest that the latter was simply running out of fuel. It is no accident that

A team photo taken at the Spanish GP in 2000.

the problems they did experience were not repeated.

Like quality, reliability is not something that can be inspected into components; it is the result of every member of the engineering organisation accepting personal responsibility for it. With just weeks between the launch of a new car and its first race, there is no time to develop reliability by track testing to provoke failures, then redesigning new parts and repeating the process. The championship is all too often won by the points gained in the first three overseas races, when the team is stretched across continents or in transit between them, and recovering from failures shown up in these races is hard to achieve before the cars return to Europe.

Achieving Ferrari's record of finishing races involves every step of the process from design through to assembly. Computer aided design and engineering permits modelling of the function of components and systems and analysis of the operating conditions, providing designers with greatly enhanced information with which to design parts. Manufacturing processes also have benefited from computer control, removing much of the variability due to human involvement. The processes are not so precise that no inspection is needed, for example, X-ray inspection of castings to check for voids and inclusions in the cast material. Composites still involve a great deal of handwork and are crit-

ically dependent on the chemical processes of mixing the resin and curing of the laminate and bonded joints. Advanced inspection techniques are being adapted from the aerospace industries, and non-destructive strength tests are required for critical components such as suspension linkages and wing mountings.

Ferrari's procedures insist that no component or system goes on the track until it has been rig tested and that it does not race until it has been proven in track testing. Some new parts are run in qualifying before being committed to a race if they provide a performance advantage. Track testing provides the raw data needed to validate the computer models and to specify rig-testing schedules. When a failure occurs, investigation determines whether the cause is design, process, manufacturing, or assembly or a gap in the knowledge of the condition under which the component operates. Provided the investigation is rigorous, failures generate new information for updating databases and procedures. Quality and reliability can only be achieved if the culture encourages people to be open and learn from errors and failures, not try and cover them up or deflect blame. Perhaps the biggest contributor to Ferrari's remarkable reliability record is the change in culture under Jean Todt's stewardship, which has eliminated the legendary political and blame-apportioning atmosphere and turned Ferrari into a team of individuals all working towards a common goal.

Ross Brawn attributes Ferrari's ever-improving reliability to two key factors: the amount of testing it carries out at Fiorano and Mugello, and Nigel Stepney, Chief Mechanic in 2000, now responsible overall for the build, servicing, and sub-assembly of the cars. He also is the person through whom all liaison passes between the racing department and the design and development office—a function critical to reliability. If there is a problem to be solved, it is communicated to the design department by Stepney, and the solutions are

passed back and integrated into the build and preparation of the cars.

Brawn says, "Reliability has been one of our strengths, and one of the reasons is the mileage we do. We test just as much as we are allowed to do by the regulations, day in, day out, either at one or both of our test tracks or at a race track, whenever we can. Fiorano and Mugello are huge assets. If I were a boss of a Formula 1 team in England, I would be looking for my own test track, because all these sophisticated systems we have on the cars now are very

LEFT: *Nigel Stepney, Chief Mechanic*

RIGHT: *All is calm in the Ferrari garage in Brazil 2000 before the cars are let out onto the track for free practice.*

time intensive, and however much you try and simulate them and create rigs to test them, the track is what it is all about. That is where you find out if it works and if it will last a race distance."

Nigel Stepney joined Ferrari in 1993 under the pre-Todt management, and he has seen the transition of the team and the change in quality standards and its affect on reliability. "In terms of engineering and working on the car, the F1-2000 was a very, very nice car," Stepney says. "It always amazes me how, from one year to the next, the car changes in details: fewer components and higher-quality components. The 2000 car was that first step where they were able to get rid off all that stuff we had had for many years from previous cars and old manufacturing methods and move up a level, away from all the old ways of doing things. The quality of production and particularly the finishing of components was much, much better.

"Also in 2000, the test team was working much better and

that had a big effect on reliability. With Fiorano we have the ability to do a lot of test work, and we started to use all the resources properly that year. We are not lacking anything—anything we want, we have—we just have to use it properly. It had taken two and a half years to get to this point from when Ross and Rory arrived, and the car was the first that was 100 percent theirs, without a lot of carry-over parts."

The need to disassemble a Formula 1 car into its individual components every 300 kilometres and at times in between, often under great pressure to do the job in minutes or seconds, is not particularly conducive to a good reliability record. Fluid and electrical systems do not take kindly to being disconnected, the couplings and connectors being the weakest links in the systems. The design has a large influence on the ease with which the mechanics are able to work on and service the cars, both at the factory and in the pit garages. One of a chief mechanic's most crucial tasks is to influence the design office to not concentrate on performance alone, but also to create a car that can be worked on easily and speedily.

"The cars are complicated and are getting more so every year, but they are also easier to work on. The thing is the fragility; the components are getting more and more fragile as the materials change, and you need more care to work with them. Putting the car together has been improved by the design, but maintenance needs more finesse as everything is on the limit of weight. We have to instill this approach on all the other departments that handle the components. The carbon suspension is typical. The components all have temperature stickers on them to check the maximum temperature they have seen, and they are all bar-coded. If the critical temperature is exceeded, they either have to be re-tested or are scrapped, and their complete history is recorded. We have various procedures for different pieces, which we are able to manage now. That is the benefit of having the people and

the systems. No one has to ask, 'What do we do with this?' We are now in the position such that, if something happens to a part, we have the technology, test equipment, and the people at a high enough level to make decisions about what to do.

"We can change an engine in about an hour and five minutes. Although it has got more complicated, we keep on at the design office, and Ross is very good on this issue, to keep a balance when the car is conceived. We want to keep the hydraulic system closed when we change an engine or gearbox to keep everything clean and oil-tight. We are making great strides with this, and it affects the design of a lot of the car. Once the system is set up, bled, and working right, we shouldn't have to touch it. There is so much involved, we still want to make improvements on the next car. We don't want to sit on our laurels and think we have come to the end of being able to improve something.

"When something goes wrong, there is always a reason and we have to find it. We make mistakes, like everybody else. We try to eliminate them with checklists, and it is a continuous learning process, such that we gradually take away the mistakes and reduce the human errors."

An equally essential part of being able to finish races is the ability of the driver to avoid losing control of the car and ending up somewhere from which he is unable to rejoin the circuit. Racing accidents often involve other drivers, but many other accidents are caused by lack of familiarity with the car and its systems and the inability to set up the car in a way that it can be driven hard for two hours. The time to learn the car is not at a race weekend, it is during testing, and Schumacher has gained the respect of his team by always being available to test, whenever required.

Says Schumacher: "When the new car is first running, you do as much testing as possible, and then, because of the amount of testing we do, there is a priority and Ross will decide the right things for me to test. I have to learn new fea-

tures on the car, away from a race if possible, when there is no time to experiment much. I do some of the endurance testing, as that is important to give the feedback of where we are.

"The cars have a lot of abilities now, within what is allowed in the rules, and it is a lot to deal with. I don't feel overloaded, but one does have to be systematic to cope with it. I am now used to the team and have grown with it. The cars evolve, so one can keep track; but if I went to a new team, it would take more time to adjust to a new car."

The reliability that has enabled Ferrari to capitalise on the performance of its cars and drivers has not come about by chance.

A Ferrari win at Imola, just down the road from Maranello, is always popular with the Tifosi.

225

16

Facilities

D rive down the busy A1 autostrada, from Milan to the Adriatic coast and the south of Italy, and the series of towns strung along the old road, the Via Emilia, have evocative names that are recognised worldwide: Parma, Modena, Bologna: ham, fast cars, and pasta sauce. Leave the autostrada at Modena, turn southwest, and arrive shortly at Maranello, which means just one thing—Ferrari. Entering this small industrial town, it is at first confusing to find the actual Ferrari factory, as almost every building is adorned with "Ferrari" or the

LEFT: *The Ferrari factory entrance today, on the Via Abetone.*

RIGHT: *[Fig. 16-2] On the gearbox tilt test rig, the performance of the gearbox wet sump oil system can be assessed while the box is subjected to simulation of representative longitudinal and lateral g-loads.*

famous prancing horse emblem. Stop and ask any of the 16,000 inhabitants, and the word "Ferrari" brings an immediate brightening of the eyes and detailed directions.

The entrance to the main factory would be familiar to anyone who had visited back in 1942, modernised to include a large Ferrari sign and a smart security and reception area. It is still entered through an almost sacred portal. But this is not the Gestione Sportiva; the Formula 1 facility is approached from opposite the new Galleria Ferrari museum, down the Via Ascari, although visitors can be escorted in the back way, across the road from the main factory, past the Ristorante Cavallino and the new Ferrari shop. For a first-time visitor,

and there are many who just come to look, it is impossible not to feel the history and passion of this place.

Scuderia Ferrari was located in Modena, Enzo Ferrari's hometown, before World War II. When he parted with Alfa Romeo in 1939, he founded Auto Avio Costruzioni (AAC), whose first project was to build the eight-cylinder 815, although Enzo was not able at that time to call it a Ferrari. Ferrari owned a piece of agricultural land near Maranello, now the site of the Fiorano test track, and in December 1942, he received planning permission for a new factory close to it. During the war, AAC manufactured small four-cylinder engines for training aircraft and petrol engine–driven

grinding machines for manufacturing ball bearings, copied from a German design. The original long, low buildings were laid out as a triangle and defined the factory that is the basis of Ferrari's road car facility today.

Success, both on the track and in the showroom, has driven a steady expansion of the facilities at Maranello. In 1972, a test track was laid out at Fiorano, and in 1982, the Formula 1 activities moved to a site opposite the track. Modernisation of the production facilities took place in the 1990s, and the new wind tunnel was completed in 1997. The most recent extension is the building of a modern logistics centre for the Formula 1 trucks and all the equipment that has to go to races; an architectural model of a completely new Formula 1 facility is to be seen on display in the existing offices.

Although the Via Ascari site houses the management, design offices, rig and dynamometer labs, and the assembly workshops of the Formula 1 team, there are major facilities for the manufacture of parts across the road in the main factory. There are very few parts of a car that Ferrari is unable to make in-house, and where it is uneconomical to do so, parent company Fiat is able to assist. An example of this is electronics and electrical components, where the investment in R&D and facilities for economic manufacture are not possible for the relatively low numbers of cars Ferrari produces. Magneti Marelli, a Fiat subsidiary, has supported Ferrari for many years, and part of it has become fully integrated into the race team.

The combination of the technical pull of racing and the economic pressures of producing road cars, even in limited numbers, has endowed the racing team with access to facilities that are unique in Formula 1. Only Team Lotus came near in recent times, but its facilities were never anything like as complete as Ferrari's. The recent direct involvement of major manufacturers in Formula 1 teams has not brought them the same advantages, as the type of facilities that might become available to them (e.g., high-volume production), are not as focused on high-performance cars and are not located on the same site. For engines, Cosworth enjoyed a similar advantage for a while, until its racing department was split off by its owner Audi and sold to Ford. BMW has integrated its Formula 1 engine department with its road engine prototyping facility, as has Honda, and thus they have many of the same facilities for engine production, but only Ferrari has the whole package.

MANUFACTURING.

Ross Brawn, unusually for the Technical Director of a Formula 1 team, is responsible for the manufacturing and production of components for the race cars. In order to protect the techniques and processes developed for making the almost aerospace-quality parts now used in the cars, he has drawn on the capabilities of Ferrari's road car production facili-

BELOW: *A map detail showing the automobile companies near Maranello, and the Mugello circuit.*

RIGHT: *An aerial view of the Maranello facilities.*

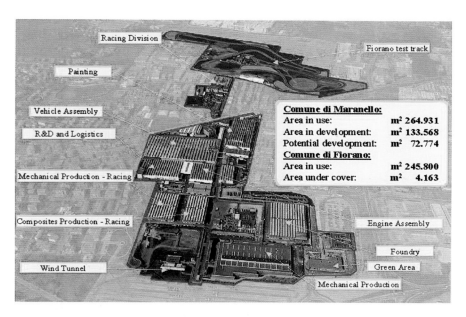

Racing Division		
Painting		Fiorano test track
Vehicle Assembly		
R&D and Logistics		
Mechanical Production - Racing		
Composites Production - Racing		Engine Assembly
Wind Tunnel		Foundry
		Green Area
		Mechanical Production

Comune di Maranello:	
Area in use:	m² 264.931
Area in development:	m² 133.568
Potential development:	m² 72.774
Comune di Fiorano:	
Area in use:	m² 245.800
Area under cover:	m² 4.163

ties. Across the road from the Gestione Sportiva and within the areas used for making parts for the sports and GT cars, there are sections for machined and fabricated components, composites, and a foundry, each dedicated to producing parts solely for the Formula 1 cars.

With around 500 V-10 engines to manufacture each year for the team and its customers, along with eight cars and a dozen gearboxes, components of which may have a life of a mere 350km, the supply chain has to be both organised down to the last tiny detail and tightly controlled to achieve the required quality. Not everything is made in-house of course, and the purchasing operation extends worldwide; Ferrari even maintains an office in the U.K. to source components from the specialist motorsport industry that has grown up there.

DESIGN.

In spite of Ferrari's often-stated advantage in having the chassis and engine design under one roof, two distinct CAD systems are used for the design of chassis and engine.

Dassault's CATIA is used for the chassis, as it provides the surfacing techniques needed for the extensive bodywork design requirements. Engine design involves much more solid modelling, particularly for castings and components with the complexity of the crankshaft. Ferrari has teamed up with Parametric Technologies UK to use its PTC CAD software.

Using two different CAD systems generates some interfacing problems and also requires dual CAM software systems to interpret CAD output and generate manufacturing data. The advantages of optimised design software evidently outweigh the problems of complete integration.

TEST RIGS.

Test rigs, whether they are engine dynamometers or simple structural test rigs, have an increasing role to play in R&D. They have always been used to simulate running conditions and measure either the dynamic performance or steady-state structural characteristics of a component or system, but with the development of ever more sophisticated measurement systems and data acquisition, they have an increasing role as a means of validating computer modelling and simulation. Now they have an increasing role as a means of validating computer modelling and simulation. All aspects of engines, transmissions, suspension, monocoques, electrical and hydraulic systems, tyres, cooling systems, etc., are today modelled during the design process to establish their performance. Strength, stiffness, power, mechanical losses, heat output, and fatigue life can all be predicted along with overall system performance, but the process is not perfect and the software used is being continuously developed and refined. Validation of the simulation techniques is required often, as well as confirmation of critical aspects of the actual component or system performance. Of all the characteristics to be confirmed, durability and reliability dominate the use of the rigs.

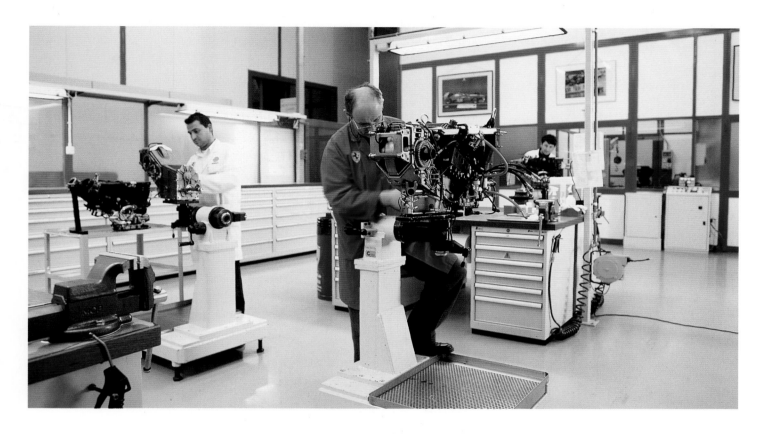

ENGINE DYNAMOMETERS.

Ferrari uses four engine dynamometers—two for R&D and two dynamic ones—employing AVL electric power absorbers. One of the latter mounts the complete powertrain, including the transmission, and is used for gearbox development as well as endurance running of engines according to full race duty cycles, defined by data acquired on the track. While this duplicates some of the functions of the gearbox power rig, described in the following section, it adds dynamic effects between the engine and gearbox, including engine-induced torsional vibration and the torque shock loads of gear changes. The other dynamic dynamometer is set below a wind tunnel, such that the airbox intrudes into it and is subjected to aerodynamic ram pressure representative of a running car. Capable of adding nearly 6 percent to the power at 350kph, it is essential to reproduce the real loads on components, as well as optimise ram pressure recovery and reproduce the interaction between intakes inside the plenum chamber.

TRANSMISSION.

There are three additional transmission test rigs.

The gearbox power rig uses hydraulic motors to drive the gearbox and absorbs the power output at the half-shafts with hydraulic pumps. In a closed-circuit system, only the gearbox mechanical losses and the hydraulic drive system loss-

es need to be supplied to run the system. Measurements of input and output torques and shaft speeds allow the efficiency of the transmission to be assessed under representative conditions, and the performance of the computer-controlled differential to be validated. Mechanical durability running also is carried out on this rig (Figures 16-8 and 16-9).

The gearbox tilt rig permits a running gearbox to be tilted in pitch and roll to simulate longitudinal and lateral g-forces. The effects on the oil system of the transmission can be studied under these simulated conditions to ensure that the pump supplies lubricant under the most extreme accelerations and that oil does not build up in the casing and create churning losses. The tilt drive system allows dynamic changes based on track data to be reproduced

(Figure 16-2 on page 227).

The gear-change rig tests the electro-hydraulic gear-change system by loading the input of the gearbox via an electric motor and slipping clutch, while measuring the torque output at the final drive. The gear-change is cycled using the car's control system to prove the functioning of electronics, hydraulics, and the mechanical components in the system (Figure 16-10).

HYDRAULICS SYSTEMS.
The complete hydraulics system, including all the hoses to be fitted to the car, can be run on a rig to check functions, cleanliness, and all joints for leaks (Figure 16-11).

There are also separate rigs for hydraulics sub-systems,

speed synchronisation, data collection (air speed and environmental parameters, balance forces, component forces, pressure, etc.), and shut-down, is controlled automatically by computer. Model attitude changes and wing incidence changes also can be set by the computer, via servos, so that a number of tests can be run sequentially without stopping the tunnel. Data reduction into whatever format is required also is automatic, and results can be viewed almost before the wind has died down.

ROLLING ROAD SYSTEM (RRS).

The RRS removes the boundary layer from the floor of the working section just ahead of the model and then maintains a nearly zero boundary layer under the model by moving the surface there at the same speed as the wind speed. Due to the suction pressure generated by the flat bottom of the model, the belt tries to lift and would touch the model if it were not sucked down onto the flat platen on which it runs. The suction is accurately adjusted to match the pressure distribution under the model to minimise the friction-generated heat of the belt running on the platen. Cooling is required to prevent the platen heating up and bowing, critically altering the shape of the air passage between the car model and the simulated road surface. The whole RRS can be yawed to simulate cornering attitudes of the car.

MOVING BELT PERFORMANCE CRITERIA.

The specifications (at left) give some insight into the level of precision required for this large and costly piece of test equipment, which represents the largest single facility investment for most Formula 1 teams. It is sometimes forgotten that wind tunnels are only simulations and therefore suffer from all their shortcomings. Their quality, the way they are used, and how well their results are interpreted are major differentiators in the performance of the current

MOVING BELT PERFORMANCE CRITERIA

Under-belt suction	Maximum under-belt suction to be 150 millibars below atmospheric pressure
Belt speed range (adjustable)	5-55m/s; 70m/s expected without model present
Belt speed variations	+/-0.1m/s about set point
Belt acceleration (deceleration) rates	2m/s²
Minimum expected belt life	100 hours
Belt width	2.4m
Maximum lateral belt travel	+/-10mm
Nominal lateral belt travel	+/-4mm
Belt change time (max, using four people)	1 hour
Distance between rollers (nominal)	5.8m
Normal operating vibration limit	10mm/s²
Maximum allowable vibration limit	30mm/s²
Flatness of belt running surface (on chassis)	+/-0.8mm—see next section
Belt outer edge surface linearity	less than +/-0.1/0.3mm

SURFACE FLATNESS REQUIREMENTS

Maximum allowable longitudinal step	+/-0.5mm
Maximum allowable transverse step	+/-0.4mm
Flatness requirement on entire area	+/-3mm
Surface waviness	1mm per 500mm
Flatness requirement on centre (width x length -10m x 2.5m)	+/-0.2mm
Flatness requirement under the belt	+/-0.8mm

TURNTABLE PERFORMANCE CRITERIA

Operational travel range	+/-6.0 (+/-8.0 preferred) degrees
Speed range	0.3-1.0 degree/sec
Acceleration	2 degrees/sec²
Positional accuracy	+/-0.03 degrees
"Zero" position accuracy	+/-0.01 degrees
Measurement accuracy	+/-0.01 degrees

BALANCE SPECIFICATION

Component	Range (N)	Sensitivity
Downforce	3450 N	1.8 mV/V
Pitch	+/-660 Nm	1.6 mV/V
Drag	1045 N	1.5 mV/V
Side Force	+/-275 N	1.5 mV/V
Yaw	+/-275 Nm	1.5 mV/V
Roll	+/-132 Nm	0.7 mV/V
Repeatability	+/-0.03 percent	
Accuracy	+/-0.03 percent	

breed of cars.

TEST TRACKS.

However good the simulations and however thorough the rig and laboratory testing, there are many aspects of any car that must be proven and optimised by driving the car on a road. Racing cars are no different, though some people are often surprised and disappointed that their new car does not perform as predicted first time out, with minimal test track time.

The tasks that can be performed best and often only on a test track include:

▫ Function checks, including post-rebuild checks prior to shipping to a race
▫ Reliability and durability
▫ Software proving
▫ Performance calibration
▫ Set-up experience (determining the trade-offs) and opti-misation of any component or system that is adjustable, including software
▫ Engine driveability assessment
▫ Wet and dry tyre testing
▫ Team training
▫ Data acquisition and simulation validation
▫ Driver familiarity with the car and experience of changes
▫ Driver training (physical preparation)
▫ New driver assessment

Ferrari owns two test facilities—Fiorano and Mugello—while no other Formula 1 team has even one. Testing at these facilities is bound by the same restrictions that are, from time to time, agreed between the teams. The advantages in overall preparedness show both by the way Ferrari is now seldom surprised by the way its car performs at a race

and by its ability to finish with remarkable regularity.

FIORANO.

The test track outside the Gestione Sportiva was built in 1972, on the original piece of land owned by Enzo Ferrari in the commune of Fiorano on which fruit trees used to grow (Figures 16-15 and 16-17). It is 2,976 metres in length, includes fifteen corners, and has an average speed, in a Formula 1 car, in excess of 160kph. The facilities include a simulated pit

LEFT TOP: [Fig. 16-15] Fiorano, Ferrari's on-site test facility.

LEFT: [Fig. 16-16] The Autodromo de Mugello nestles in the foothills of the Apennines. Along with Fiorano, Ferrari has test facilities representative of virtually all conditions experienced on race circuits.

RIGHT: [Fig. 16-17] Testing at Fiorano. Enzo Ferrari's house and office are in the background.

garage; start line, with FIA starting lights; computerised timing; ten CCTV cameras; and full safety provisions. Ferrari recently installed a computer-controlled watering system, capable of maintaining any constant wet track condition on any part of the circuit.

MUGELLO.

Ferrari's second test track is the Mugello circuit, purchased in 1989. One hundred thirty kilometers from Maranello on the road to Florence, Mugello nestles in the foothills of the Apennines. It is 5,245 metres in length and incorporates fifteen corners and a 1.1km straight. The circuit is better suited than Fiorano for testing high-speed aerodynamic and cornering characteristics and engine performance. There are all the facilities one would expect at a modern racing circuit, including those for timing, CCTV, safety, and hospitality (Figure 16-16).

The importance of these test facilities to Ferrari and indeed of Ferrari to Italy can be gauged by the Italian government's relaxation of a 70-decibel noise restriction imposed on other circuits. Guests at a local hotel in Maranello are often woken by the rising and falling wail of an 18,000rpm V-10 hard at work. The sound continues all day, on and off, and no one in the town raises an eyebrow, let alone complains!

17

Race and Chassis Statistics

The seventeen Grands Prix of the 2000 World Championship produced the results for Ferrari shown in the table below.

RACE	CIRCUIT	MS RACE	MS QUALIFYING	RB RACE	RB QUALIFYING	MS POINTS	RB POINTS	FERRARI POINTS
Australian GP	Melbourne	1	3	2	4	10	6	16
Brazilian GP	Interlagos	1	3	R	4	10	0	10
San Marino GP	Imola	1	2	4	4	10	3	13
British GP	Silverstone	3	5	R	1	4	0	4
Spanish GP	Catalunya	5	1	3	3	2	4	6
European GP	Nurburgring	1	2	4	4	10	3	13
Monaco GP	Monte Carlo	R	1	2	6	0	6	6
Canadian GP	Montreal	1	1	2	3	10	6	16
French GP	Magny Cours	R	1	3	3	0	4	4
Austrian GP	A1 Ring	R	4	3	3	0	4	4
German GP	Hockenheim	R	2	1	18	0	10	10
Hungarian GP	Hungaring	2	1	4	5	6	3	9
Belgian GP	Spa Francorchamp	2	4	R	10	6	0	6
Italian GP	Monza	1	1	R	2	10	0	10
USA GP	Indianapolis	1	1	2	2	10	6	16
Japanese GP	Suzuka	1	1	4	4	10	3	13
Malaysian GP	Sepang	1	1	3	4	10	4	14
Total						108	62	170

LEFT: *When it rains, driving skill can outweigh car performance. Both of Ferrari's drivers are masters in the rain, and they achieved a 1-2 finish in Canada.*

FIA FORMULA 1 WORLD CHAMPIONSHIP, 2000

Manufacturers' World Championship: Ferrari
Drivers' World Championship: Michael Schumacher
Rubens Barrichello, fourth

Build

A total of eight chassis of the 651-series Ferrari were built as the F1-2000s used for racing and testing. The total distances run on each chassis include races and testing in 2000 and testing carried out in 2001 while the new cars for 2001 were being built. In addition to the eight chassis, a total of 400 Tipo 049 engines were built, plus 100 engines for Sauber. Twelve gearboxes were built for the cars.

Chassis No.	Kilometero
651-198	2,311
651-199	15,238
651-200	1,196
651-201	15,051
651-202	7,105
651-203	4,430
651-204	1,128
651-205	3,828
Total	**50,287**

The chassis used by each driver were as follows.

Race	MS Chassis No.	RB Chassis No.
Australian GP	200	199
Brazilian GP	201	199
San Marino GP	200	199
British GP	200	199
Spanish GP	200	199
European GP	200	202
Monaco GP	198	202
Canadian GP	203	202
French GP	203	202
Austrian GP	204	202
German GP	200	202
Hungarian GP	203	202
Belgian GP	205	202
Italian GP	205	202
USA GP	205	203
Japanese GP	205	203
Malaysian GP	205	200

LEFT: *Hungarian Grand Prix, Hungaroring. Michael Schumacher second, Rubens Barrichello fourth. In Hungary, Mika Hakkinen was just too quick, but second place kept Schumacher's title hopes alive at a critical stage in the season.*

Once the season is completed and sufficient new cars are built to cover testing duties, the old cars can be stood down from the duty of testing new parts, systems, and software and pensioned off. One or two are supplied to sponsors for promotional purposes; one or two go to museums, including the Galleria Ferrari, in Maranello; and eventually, two years minimum after the end of the season, the remainder are put up for sale to private customers. The price for an F1-2000 was "over $2 million," and Ferrari has no difficulty in finding customers.

Epilogue

After the 2000 season, Ferrari presented the top level of motorsport with a dilemma. Formula 1 is one of the last remaining series that has a significant technical component. Most others are single car, single engine, production car–based or based on heavily performance- or cost-limited formulae. As a result, Formula 1 attracts manufacturer support from those car companies and industry suppliers that wish to differentiate their products with a technical slant, even if it is only by association.

The funding this has liberated has enabled the teams with major support from the automobile industry to develop their technical sophistication to such an extent that those who lack the support are unable to compete, and the cars have become too perfect and the racing too predictable. Ferrari has emerged with a technical dominance in the past few years that has not only won both the World Championship titles each year since 2000, but has taken the team to a point where not even McLaren-Mercedes or Williams-BMW could stay with them. The dilemma is that the technical pre-eminence and virtually unlimited budgets that characterise this top-level sport threaten not only small-

er modestly funded teams, but also fans' interest in watching races.

Whether this situation has been bad for Formula 1 depends on one's viewpoint. If one follows Formula 1 for the racing spectacle, it has undoubtedly suffered, although the inevitable ebb and flow of competitiveness and changes in FIA rules for 2003 have made this season—still underway at the time of this writing—exciting and unpredictable. It's quite a change from the two years that preceded it. If one admires the way Ferrari has recovered from the low point of the early 1990s against all the predictions and has continued to apply a truly professional approach to technology man-

agement, these are indeed exciting times. What is clear, however, is that it is the racing spectacle that attracts followers and viewers in sufficient numbers to justify the industry and sponsor funding upon which the sport depends, and if this is to continue, technology may have to be traded for sport.

Formula 1 had become a victim of its own success. Of all the sports vying for sponsorship dollars, motorsport is the only one that offers such an enticing combination of danger, technology, athleticism, psychology, and skill. Its success on TV, brought about by the efforts of Bernie Ecclestone, ensured that it attracted the big marketing budgets of the tobacco companies, as well as those of the automobile industry. The income generated by the teams and the technical

partnerships that developed accelerated their commercial and technical professionalism and attracted drivers who matched this professional approach to the sport. But it was the sport that suffered, as the emphasis moved from driver skill to car technology.

There are many opinions about where the blame lies for an apparent loss of excitement in the races in Formula 1 and, indeed, in many other motor racing series. High levels of downforce and the inability of a car to corner at high speed close behind another, along with a lack of being able to slide the cars, are reckoned to be the main culprits, but it is more complex than this. Racing in the 1960s and '70s involved cars that had simple throttle actuation cables, manual gearboxes, and were relatively unreliable; engines,

LEFT: *The teamwork that helped Michael Schumacher clinch the 2002 championship in France with six races remaining was quickly and successfully applied to Rubens Barrichello to make sure he claimed second place. The pair are shown here celebrating their 1-2 finish at the season-opening race in Australia in 2000.*

RIGHT: *The F2003-GA—named after Giovanni Agnelli, Fiat's charismatic late president and Ferrari supporter—is one of the most beautiful Ferrari Grand Prix cars in recent times.*

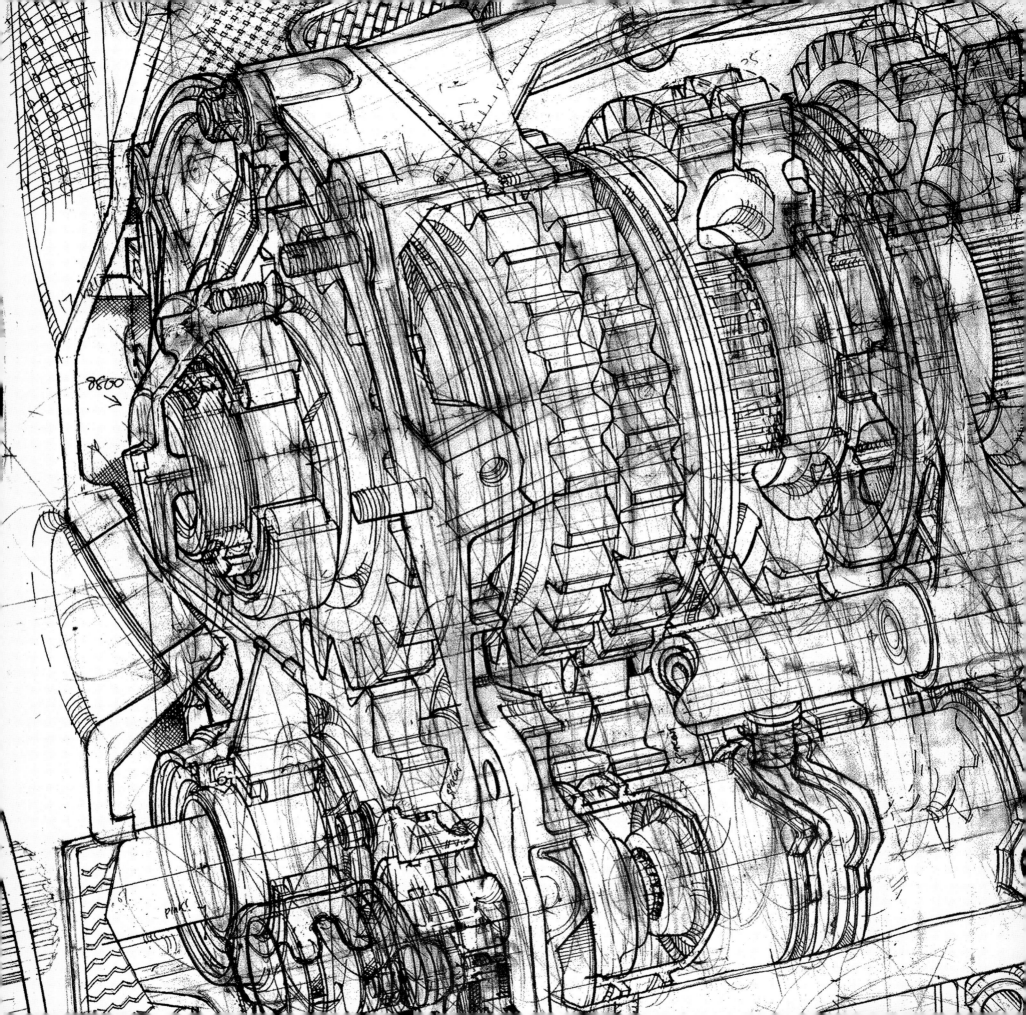

gearboxes, brakes, cooling, and tyres often featured in race incidents and retirements. Cars ran out of fuel with regularity, and communication between driver and pits was by unreadable pit signals and a fair bit of arm waving. By 2002, the level of perfection and technical preparation of the cars and the elimination of potential driver errors meant that the cars lined up in qualifying speed order, and once they started (under the control of the "launch" system and traction control) one could expect them to proceed in that order, with the gaps between cars increasing with laps completed. Pit stops to refuel and change tyres introduced some uncertainty, but even these now tend to go as planned. Barring accidents, human errors, and some car failures, the cars will finish in the order they started.

Much of the excitement of racing in the "good old days" was a result of the uncertainty of almost amateur racing. Drivers missed gears, slid wide, over-revved their engines, wore out their tyres, and overcooked the brakes, allowing the car behind to at least temporarily overtake. Most of this excitement was not seen on TV or watched by hundreds of thousands of spectators, but reported by enthusiastic journalists in magazines. Worldwide TV coverage, sponsorship, and the extensive involvement by the motor industry have increased the stakes and insisted on a high level of professional performance, both in the technical departments of the car and engine manufacturers and from the drivers. Unpredictability had decreased, and it was this that the FIA set out to introduce again.

For 2003, the FIA announced the most wide-ranging changes to the Formula 1 regulations for more than a decade. The 2002 economic climate was such that two Formula 1 teams—Prost and Arrows—went out of business, and with falling TV audiences and nervous sponsors, both current and potential, the FIA stepped in to ensure the long-term viability of Formula 1. Some of the blame for falling TV revenues

had been laid at Ferrari's door, after it wrapped up the 2002 World Championship at the French GP with six races still to go. The only suspense for race fans was to see whether Ferrari could bring Rubens Barrichello into second place, which was easily accomplished. Not only did the cost of Formula 1 racing need to be reduced, to enable the smaller teams to survive and keep the numbers on the grid in excess of twenty cars, but the sheer entertainment value of the sport needed a thorough overhaul. And that is what it got, starting at:

A change in the points awarded for both Championships from 10, 6, 4, 3, 2, 1 for the first six finishers to 10, 8, 6, 5, 4, 3, 2, 1 for the first eight finishers.

The introduction of one flying lap, single-car qualifying to determine the grid.

No work may be carried out on the cars between final qualifying and the race, except under strict FIA supervision, to ensure major parts are not replaced nor prohibited parts introduced. Tyres and fuel load to remain unchanged for the race.

Tyre suppliers may bring more than two compound choices to cover all their teams, allowing for differences in chassis characteristics. Teams may still only assess two compounds each during practice and select one for qualifying and the race.

Two-way radio voice communication will be monitored by the FIA and will be available to the host broadcaster. This will aid the policing of a ban on team orders.

Part of the FIA's case is that much of the technology being developed in parallel by several teams and engine manufacturers is of no interest to the paying public. Regulations to reduce the cost of developments that do not contribute to the spectacle will continue to be negotiated between teams and the FIA. Because the money that funds Formula 1 ultimately comes from the public's pocket, it

A detail of Tony Matthews's working drawing of the F1-2000 gearbox.

rules of engagement. There will be a greatly increased emphasis on reliability and overall preparedness, which Ferrari, with its two test tracks and rigorous test policy, excels at. In Michael Schumacher, it has one of the smartest drivers in the history of Grand Prix racing, and his relationship with master strategist Ross Brawn is already the stuff of legends. The unpredictability introduced by the new sporting regulations will undoubtedly make life more difficult, but between them they will devise how best to exploit the new regulations.

Ferrari's approach to competing for the World Championship is first and foremost professional, and it is this that has brought success in a sport that has not always benefited from an abundance of this attribute. It may be argued that Formula 1 has suffered as a sport as it has become more professional, but the 2003 season demonstrated that sporting contest is recovering as Ferrari's competitors catch up with its methods and performance.

Ross Brawn has said that this is a situation that all at Ferrari relish. Overwhelming superiority is wonderful once in a while, but it is inevitable that the competition catches up, and a strong fight is something he and his engineers rise to, and it is good for Formula 1. The Scuderia exudes confidence based on a happy, dedicated group of senior engineers, the world's best driver and a highly competitive number two, and a team of engineers, technicians, and mechanics with all the passion the Italian nation can muster. Enzo Ferrari would have revelled in the situation.

would be wise to ensure that they feel they are getting good value for it.

The FIA has been determined to improve the human aspects of the sport by interpreting the regulation that states that "the driver must drive the car alone and unaided" in the most wide-ranging way and then enforcing it. With the sporting regulation changes, more things deviate from each team's race plan because a car's position on the grid is determined by a single lap carrying the fuel the team decides to start the race with, after which the car is isolated until the race. Qualifying now becomes part of the race, with a wide choice of refuelling strategies possible, and that has spiced up the racing.

Will Ferrari's relative competitiveness be affected? Probably not a lot. The managerial, technical, and racing organisation that has been built up appears to be both flexible and robust and well able to adapt to a new set of

LLEFT: The 2000 season was followed by two dominant years when Ferrari and Michael Schumacher could do little wrong. In 2003, Williams-BMW and McLaren-Mercedes upped their games, and Juan Pablo Montoya emerged as Schumacher's main challenger for the championship. Here the two battle it out at Monza.

RIGHT: The F2003-GA's cooling gills evoke styling features from famous Ferraris of the past.

Time will tell where the real magic lies. —**John Lennon, 1940-1980**

Index

INDEX OF ILLUSTRATION CREDITS

REFERENCES

Ref 0.1   Pomeroy, Laurence, *The Grand Prix Car, Volumes 1 and 2*, (London: Temple Press Books Ltd., 1954)

Ref 0.2   Wright, Peter, *Formula 1 Technology*, (Warrendale, Pennsylvania: SAE 2001)

Ref 7.1   Boretti, Alberto.A (Fiat Research Centre, Engines Dept.), *Parametric Design of FIA F1 Engines* (Warrendale, Pennsylvania: SAE MSEC2002-01-3315)

Ref 9.   www.grandprix.com

Ref 14.2   Milliken, W.F., and D.L. Milliken, *Race Car Vehicle Dynamics*, (Warrendale, Pennsylvania: SAE, 1995)

Ref 14.3   www.millikenresearch.com